What the press says about Harlequin Romances…

"…clean, wholesome fiction…always with an upbeat, happy ending."
—*San Francisco Chronicle*

"…a work of art."
—*The Globe & Mail*, Toronto

"Nothing quite like it has happened since *Gone With the Wind*…"
—*Los Angeles Times*

"…among the top ten…"
—*International Herald-Tribune*, Paris

"Women have come to trust these clean, easy-to-read love stories about contemporary people, set in exciting foreign places."
—*Best Sellers*, New York

OTHER

Harlequin Romances

by ANNE HAMPSON

Many of these titles are available at your local bookseller or through the Harlequin Reader Service.

For a free catalogue listing all available Harlequin Romances, send your name and address to:

HARLEQUIN READER SERVICE,
M.P.O. Box 707, Niagara Falls, N.Y. 14302
Canadian address: Stratford, Ontario, Canada N5A 6W4

or use order coupon at back of books.

Call of
the Outback

by

ANNE HAMPSON

Harlequin Books

TORONTO • LONDON • NEW YORK • AMSTERDAM • SYDNEY

Original hardcover edition published in 1976
by Mills & Boon Limited

ISBN 0-373-02082-1

Harlequin edition published July 1977

Printed in U.S.A.

CHAPTER ONE

FIVE o'clock at last! Sally Prentice covered her type-writer, grabbed her handbag from the top drawer of her desk and, with a quick, 'so long,' to her colleague, Tracy, she hurried from the office, took the lift to the ground floor and within five minutes she was on the bus.

The day had dragged, simply because it was the last day before her holiday. Not that she was going any-where, but the idea of a complete rest was attractive in itself.

Sixteen mornings when she could lie in bed for an extra hour! Sixteen days in which to catch up with jobs about the house, with some reading in between, and some visiting.

'You're early,' was the surprised greeting she re-ceived as she entered the small house she shared with Joyce. 'You've not come on your normal bus.'

'I caught the earlier one. Today has dragged so abominably that I couldn't get out of the office quickly enough.' A deep, contented sigh escaped her. 'Oh, but I'm looking forward to the next fortnight!'

Joyce smiled; she herself had been in for over an hour. A schoolteacher at the Infant School across the way, she was fortunate enough to be home each day by a quarter past four, having spent the last half hour tidying up her classroom.

And so the tea was invariably ready when Sally arrived, and today was no exception. In the alcove in

5

the kitchen-cum-dining-room the table was daintily laid, and a mouthwatering chicken salad met Sally's expectant glance. There were strawberries and cream to follow, then coffee.

'You're a real brick, Joyce. I was certainly lucky when you answered my advertisement for someone to share this house with me.'

Joyce bit her lip, and a slight frown settled on her brow, causing her friend to look askance at her. She seemed unable to phrase whatever it was she had to say, but presently she looked at Sally and murmured, a hint of apology in her tone,

'Darrell and I are planning to get married at the end of August.'

A silence fell, but only fleetingly. Sally, her face brightening, and a ready smile leaping to her lips, told her friend that she was delighted with the news.

'It's wonderful, Joyce. You were obviously pulling my leg when you said you were only good friends,' she added teasingly, but Joyce was shaking her head.

'No, Sally, that was the truth. Darrell's proposal came as a complete surprise to me.'

'But you wanted it to come?'

'Of course. Yet I never believed it would; he's always talked as if he's perfectly happy with his mum.' She smiled reflectively. 'However, last evening he asked me to marry him. I wanted to tell you when I came in, but I felt so guilty——'

'Nonsense,' broke in Sally admonishingly. 'We've both known that one day this partnership must come to an end. Why, it could have been I who'd been lucky enough to have a proposal, couldn't it?'

Joyce nodded her head, hesitating for a space before saying,

'There's no chance...?' She stopped, and made a grimace. 'I'm not over-endowed with tact, am I?'

Sally shrugged her shoulders.

'Paul and I aren't really suited, Joyce, and that's why we don't attempt to bring any sort of intimacy into our relationship. I like him—no use denying it, but although I sometimes wish he would ask me to marry him, I know, deep down inside, that the chances of a successful marriage between us are not at all good. And so it would be too risky by far—don't you agree? One doesn't leave so important a thing as marriage to chance.'

'No, indeed not. But I've always had the impression that you regard him as rather more than a friend.'

'Yes, I admit it,' returned Sally with a small sigh. 'Yet I know that if he did ask me to marry him, and I accepted, I shouldn't be one hundred per cent happy about it.'

Joyce said nothing and Sally went on to ask where she and Darrell were going to live when they were married.

'With his mother—although neither of us is content with the arrangement. We'd both like to be on our own, and Darrell's mother agrees that it's preferable. However, as we haven't the money to buy a house we've no choice.'

A short while later Sally was in the bathroom, washing her face and hands. She had inserted the advertisement in the newspaper three years previously because, at eighteen, she had not been in a position to pay all the expenses out of her salary. The house had belonged to her parents, who died within six months of one another when Sally was only two years old. Her parents had had as a paying guest a distant cousin who managed to retain the tenancy even though she was unwilling to care for the child. In consequence Sally had been given a home with a foster-mother, but when her house became vacant on the death of its occupant she had moved in. Having Joyce had eased Sally's purse and the whole arrangement had been a most happy one. Now, however, Sally knew that although she could manage to run the house out of her own earnings, she was certainly going to miss her friend's contribution.

Having washed, Sally entered her bedroom, carrying her dress over her arm. She always changed after coming from the office and she now took a crisp cotton dress from the wardrobe. This she put on, pleased with the way it showed off her tan, a tan acquired by lying on the tiny lawn in a deck-chair, for the weather had been sunny and hot from the end of May until the end of June. So at week-ends she and Joyce had managed to spend a few hours sunbathing. A week of incessant rain had just ended and once again the weather was as good as it had ever been.

'Gosh, I do look forward to eating this appetising meal!' Sally was exclaiming when, after brushing her hair and applying a little colour to her lips, she came down to the little kitchenette. 'I've got so used to a meal ready prepared for me.'

'Aren't you going to get someone else in?' inquired Joyce.

'I haven't had time to think about it yet.' Sally sat down and helped herself to a bread roll from the basket. 'I've got so used to you that I expect I'd be forever finding fault with someone else,' she added with a self-deprecating laugh.

'Who's talking nonsense now?' chided Joyce. 'You,

8

my love, could get on with anyone.'

'I'm certainly not getting on with my boss very well at the present time,' returned Sally with a grimace. 'He's a slave-driver if ever there was one. His trouble is that he's got a nagging wife, so when he comes to work he likes to assert his authority. It does something for his ego, I expect.'

'He's never been a nice boss, though, has he?'

'No, but he and I have managed to get along reasonably well. He's become intolerable lately and we all believe that things have deteriorated at home. I'm sorry for him in a way, but I'm sure I'll be giving in my notice soon. Monday mornings are terrible—after he's had a week-end with his wife.'

'Poor man. Still, he's no right to take it out on his staff.'

'Never mind,' said Sally cheerfully. 'I've a fortnight's holiday—sixteen days counting the three week-ends—before I have to go back.'

The two girls chatted while having their meal, then Sally took over the task of clearing away and washing the dishes, while her friend settled down to the marking of some books.

'I didn't look in the box to see if there was any mail,' called Joyce from the living room. 'Not that *I'm* expecting any. There might be something for you, though.'

'I shouldn't think so—unless it's a bill! I'll go and see in a few minutes.'

There was a letter in the box on the front door, and a tender smile spread over Sally's face as she took it out and closed the box again.

'So you did have one,' observed Joyce, glancing up from the book she had on her knee.

'From my foster-mother.'

'Ah ... that's why you're smiling.'

'She's a gem, isn't she?'

'One of the best. You were lucky, Sally.'

'I know it.'

'I suppose that wasn't altogether the right thing to say——' Joyce looked faintly contrite. 'It certainly wasn't lucky when you lost your parents like that. What I meant was that you were fortunate to get someone as kind as Mrs Rotherham for a foster-mother.'

'Yes...' Having slit the envelope, Sally withdrew the letter and became absorbed in it. 'She wants me to visit her as soon as possible, but to phone her immediately.'

'Immediately—this evening?'

'I expect so.' Sally was frowning. 'It sounds most mysterious. The letter's short and completely uninformative.'

'Do you think she might be ill?' asked Joyce anxiously.

'I don't know.' Automatically Sally was replacing the letter in its envelope. 'I intended spending a week-end with her, as you know, but I'd decided to do some of my jobs first, so that I'd enjoy the visit more, knowing I hadn't to come back to a whole lot of hard work. However, I'll go and telephone her now and find out when she wants me.'

The telephone box was only a few hundred yards from the house, and Sally was soon speaking to her foster-mother.

'I thought you'd ring this evening, darling!' The voice was young and light. 'Can you come over to-morrow, and stay until Sunday or even Monday?

You're not working, so there's no problem, is there? I have got the dates right?' she added uncertainly. 'It is today you started your annual break?'

'Yes, that's right. What is it, Mum? Nothing serious, obviously.'

'It's very serious, but I can't talk to you properly on the phone. In any case, I've to be at work in less than an hour's time.'

'You're still working at that restaurant? I thought you said you were giving it up because you were tired of working in the evenings.'

'I know I did, but the money's good—and the tips are even better. When people have wined and dined well they're usually in a generous mood.'

'I'll be over to see you, then, tomorrow. But I'm so curious, pet, so you must give me a clue——'

'All I shall say is this, by way of a warning to you and to give you something to think about: remember you once promised me that if ever I needed your help, you would be there on the instant to give it,' and on that note the voice faded and the only sound was that of the receiver being replaced on its rest.

Walking home thoughtfully, and slowly, Sally re called the exact words to which her foster-mother had just referred.

'You've done so much for me, darling, that if ever I can do anything to repay you—if ever you should need help, I shall be there on the instant, no matter what it costs me.'

Well, it would appear that her foster-mother now needed help . . . and yet she had not sounded troubled in any way at all.

'It doesn't make sense,' she was commenting to Joyce a short while later. 'Mum's not troubled, yet she says it's something serious she wants to see me about.'

'Sounds strange. But as there's nothing you can do until tomorrow there isn't anything to be gained by trying to fathom out the mystery. Thank goodness she's not ill. I admit I was more than a little afraid she'd had some kind of a mishap.'

'So was I,' returned Sally, inordinately relieved that her foster-mother had sounded so cheerful and well. 'I can only think,' she added musingly as the idea occurred to her, 'that it's something to do with Nicole.'

'Her own daughter?'

'My foster-sister, yes.'

'She's still at school, surely? I mean, Mrs Rotherham didn't have her when she and her husband first took you into their home?'

'No. They'd been married for five years and didn't think they'd have any children of their own. Then when I was four years old they had Nicole. As you know, Mr Rotherham died soon afterwards. I scarcely remember him, and Nicole doesn't remember him at all, naturally.'

'When does Nicole leave school?'

'Next week.'

'I can't see her being in any sort of trouble, Sally. From what you've told me at various times she seems to be a model daughter.'

'So she is—a rare pet, like her mother. Nicole's the image of her mother, too—with lovely auburn hair and hazel eyes.'

No more was said, and early the following morning Sally left the house, after having breakfasted with Joyce. A few hours later she was at the home of her foster-mother, the small, terraced house in which she had spent a wonderfully happy childhood. And she supposed she would have been living here still had not her foster-mother strongly advised her to take possession of her own house.

'If you let it to someone you can't get them out,' she warned. 'And you never know just when you'll want it because something might happen to me, or you might want to get married. The house would then be there for your husband to share if it so happened that he couldn't afford to buy one.' Sally had argued, for she had no wish to leave this secure haven, but in the end she had succumbed to her foster-mother's good and well-meaning advice and moved into her own little home.

'Come in, pet!' Mrs Rotherham, small and dainty and looking far younger than her forty-eight years, received her foster-daughter with open arms. 'I'll have coffee and toasted teacakes ready in a jiff!'

It was over this small repast that Sally heard the story of Nicole and her pen-friend, Ray Lander, an Australian from the Outback. With the keenest interest Sally listened, mentally trying to form a picture of the vast cattle station of which her foster-mother was speaking, where Ray Lander worked with his brother, Kort. This older man—eleven years his brother's senior—appeared to be something of an autocrat who, having decided he would never marry and therefore Ray must be his heir, considered himself to be in a position to choose Ray's wife for him. And it very soon occurred to Sally that this Ray, who was only twenty-two years of age, was rebelling and, in consequence, was willing to marry a girl whom he had never even seen. Having mentioned her idea to Mrs Rotherham as soon as she had an opportunity, Sally received a swift agreement from her foster-mother.

'That's exactly the way I saw it!' she said triumphantly. 'Nicole won't have it; she says that Ray thinks a great deal about her and therefore he wants to marry her.'

'That's nonsense!'

'It appears to be——' Mrs Rotherham hesitated, rather to Sally's surprise. 'Nicole's kept nothing from me, Sally. She's shown me all his recent letters. And I must in fairness say that he seems a very genuine young man. He's wealthy, and will be wealthier still, if his brother never marries, that is. So I'm naturally interested, in that, should Nicole marry him, she would have a life not only of comfort, but of luxury.'

'I don't understand,' said Sally, puzzled. 'At first you seemed dead set against Nicole going over to this cattle station, but now you say you're interested——'

'I haven't finished, pet,' intervened Mrs Rotherham. 'But firstly, I'll come out with the most important aspect of this business. I want you to go over there with Nicole and see how the land lies——'

'Me?' ejaculated Sally without thinking about that promise she had once made. 'That's absolutely impossible!'

'Your promise, dear,' murmured her foster-mother, and there was a distinct gleam of triumph in her eyes, although there was a trace of amusement as well.

Sally coloured slightly.

'I know, Mum, but——'

'And now,' cut in Mrs Rotherham, 'I'll get on with the main part of the story.'

'Very well,' with a sigh of resignation. Sally had not lived with Mrs Rotherham for sixteen years without having learned that when she set her heart on something she invariably managed to succeed in her aim.

'So Nicole doesn't mind my going with her?' Sally was saying five minutes later, and her foster-mother shook her head.

'It was she who suggested it. She's always been a sensible child, as you know, and she's never done anything to cause me anxiety; so when she put forward the idea that, as Ray had proposed marriage, she should go to Australia and meet him, she knew I'd be out of my mind with worry if she went alone. She also knew that I wouldn't go with her as I'm terrified of flying——'

'I take it,' interrupted Sally, 'that this Ray has offered to send Nicole her air fare?'

'Of course. He's willing to pay for two first class tickets.'

Sally nodded, and asked her foster-mother to continue, which she did, telling Sally that although Ray had said very little about Kort in his letters, it was obvious that he was going to be a fly in the ointment, since he had someone else lined up as a suitable wife for his brother who would eventually become the boss of Grey River Downs, one of the largest cattle ranches in the Outback.

'I still think that, as Ray's only doing this as an act of rebellion against the imperious, high-handed attitude of his brother, his offer should be turned down by Nicole.' Sally, who had again been listening with the keenest interest, spoke at last, shaking her head as she did so, an illustration of her total dislike of the situation.

'That's how I felt at first, and indeed, it's how I often feel now,' admitted her foster-mother. 'But Nicole has set her heart on taking that trip to Australia. It could be that she's merely seizing the

15

opportunity of experiencing adventure—you know what the teenagers are like these days. On the other hand, it could be that she's fallen in love with Ray——'

'How can anyone fall in love through correspondence?' Sally wanted to know, her practical mind utterly rejecting such a possibility. 'Honestly, Mum, the whole thing sounds crazy to me.'

A sigh escaped the woman sitting there, toying with a piece of hot buttered teacake.

'There's only one way to settle the matter,' she commented logically at last, 'and that is for Nicole to go over, meet Ray, stay as a visitor at Grey River Downs for a while so that she can get to know him, and make up her mind both about him and the life she'll have to live out there. This latter's most important, I think you'll agree?'

Sally nodded; she was frowning heavily, because she envisaged so many, many snags.

'I believe it's a very lonely life.'

'True, as I've pointed out to Nicole. *She* then points out that she's not one for the gay life—dancing and the rest, and I must admit that she has a point there. Like you, she's a home bird, so I don't really think there'd be any problems in that direction.'

Sally was still frowning.

'How did Nicole come to start writing to Ray?'

'Well, lots of the girls at school have pen-friends abroad and Nicole wanted to be in the swim. So when a friend of hers emigrated to Australia with her parents about six or seven months ago Nicole not only asked this girl to write to her but also asked her to find an Australian who would be willing to write to her. Nicole expected it to be a girl, of a similar age to herself, but this friend of hers had found Ray. He wrote to Nicole, who was naturally thrilled that so important a man should want to write to her, and she accepted him as her pen-friend. Her school friend had, it seemed, been taken by her parents on a trip to the Centre—Alice Springs and all that part.' They broke down and were taken in and helped by the owner of Grey River Downs, staying at the ranch for two or three days until their vehicle was repaired. Nicole's friend—I can't remember her name at present—— Oh, yes, it's Valerie. Well, Valerie became friendly with Ray and she must have thought that he'd do as a pen-friend for Nicole, whose photograph she happened to have in a small album she was carrying in her luggage.'

'So Ray saw Nicole's photograph before he began writing to her?'

'Yes, that's right.'

'She's very pretty,' murmured Sally, almost to herself.

'I think so.' But Mrs Rotherham's eyes were on her foster-daughter's face. She had always been of the opinion that Sally was more than pretty: she was beautiful, with her heart-shaped face and faintly slanting blue eyes—big, widely-spaced eyes that never seemed to have anything to hide, so open and honest were they in their expression. Her skin was unblemished, her forehead high and clear, her eyelashes long and curling. All this, and honey-gold hair which kinked naturally so that, wearing it short as she did, it gave her an elfin-like appearance which, to her proud foster-mother, was inordinately attractive. She could have the pick of the men, she had once affectionately told her, but Sally, flushing under the compliment,

17

had immediately changed the subject.

'This man Kort,' Sally mused, 'I do feel that, if Nicole does go to the ranch, she's in for trouble from him.'

'I feel the same. Nicole is very sensible, though. She's no starry-eyed little thing whose optimism far outstrips her common sense. She wants to meet Ray, and as he's sending her the fare it's understandable that she's keen on taking the trip. He's promised that if she doesn't want to marry him he'll put her on a plane for home just whenever she asks him to.'

'He couldn't be fairer than that—but of course he couldn't do anything else, either.'

'That's true.'

'I rather think that this Kort would prefer an Australian for a sister-in-law.'

'Undoubtedly.'

'Has he raised any objections to the idea of Nicole going over there to meet Ray?'

'I'll be honest, Sally, he's said outright that the idea's ridiculous.'

'He doesn't believe it's possible to fall in love merely by an exchange of letters?'

'Something of the kind.' Mrs Rotherham hesitated. 'To be frank, he sounds the sort of man who's cynical about love anyway. Imagine a man of thirty-three having given up the idea of marriage for himself. It's unnatural, for one thing.'

'A lot of those tough Outback cattle graziers live only for their work. They're self-sufficient and have no place for women in their scheme of things.'

'It's perhaps a very good thing for Ray, though. He'll inherit everything.'

Sally nodded, then both she and her foster-mother

glanced at the door as a light step could be heard outside it.

'Sally!' exclaimed Nicole happily. 'So you came at once! We knew you would, of course! Aren't you excited at the idea of going to——'

'Hold on a moment!' Sally lifted a warning hand. 'I haven't yet made any promises, if that's what you're looking so pleased about. If this friend of yours is willing to pay two first class fares then surely there's someone else you can get to accompany you...?' Sally allowed her voice to trail off to a resigned silence as through her own words she heard her foster-mother say,

'The promise, dear.'

'What about my job, Mum?' she protested feebly. 'I'll lose it.'

'And be rid of that dreadful, frustrated old boss of yours! With your qualifications you can get another job as easy as that!' Mrs Rotherham snapped her fingers, and Sally, fast capitulating, made one last stand.

'My house ... I could be away from it for months —if Nicole takes time to make up her mind——'

'Joyce will look after it for you.'

'She's getting married in August, and they're going to live with Darrell's mother.'

Mrs Rotherham's eyes flickered.

'Why are they going to live with Darrell's mother?'

'They can't get a house——' Sally stopped, heaved a great sigh and said, 'All right, you needn't say it! Joyce and Darrell will be delighted to take over my house.'

'That's right, darling,' returned her foster-mother with a sweet smile. 'And so you see there really isn't one single drawback to your accompanying Nicole to Australia, is there?'

'No, Mum,' replied Sally in defeated tones, 'there isn't.'

Strangely, by the time she was leaving on Monday morning Sally was really looking forward to the trip. She had gradually come round to the fact that she was actually most fortunate. For a long while she had been dissatisfied with her job, and more than once she had expressed the wish that 'something exciting would happen'. And now here it was. Difficulties in plenty she could envisage, but she also saw some pleasantness in seeing a new country, and a new way of life—that which was lived by the squatocracy whose domains were so vast that they were often as large as countries, with their owners ruling over them like the feudal lords of old.

Later in the day she telephoned her boss and gave in her notice, promising to send it in writing straight away. He said little and she was relieved. As it was Monday, whatever he had to say would undoubtedly have been unpleasant.

Arrangements went forward without a hitch. Ray was to meet them at a place called Roeville, which they would reach after taking a long journey on a coach. He would then fly them to the cattle station where they would stay as guests of his brother.

'You do realize,' said Mrs Rotherham to her daughter the night before the girls' departure, 'that if you don't meet with Kort's approval your choice is going to be even more difficult?'

Sally, who was spending the last night at her old home, nodded her head understandingly, but Nicole cast her mother an inquiring glance and said,

'I don't know what you mean?'

'If you marry Ray without his brother's approval you could find life difficult, owing to the probable animosity you'd have to face.'

'Also,' murmured Sally, 'Kort might take it into his head to find another heir. I expect there are other relatives to whom he could leave his share of the property.'

'Ray would still be well off.'

'But he might like the idea of being better off,' put in her mother.

'He's not like that, darling—— Yes, I know what you're going to say—I can't have formed a true reading of his character from letters alone. And I admit it; that's why I must have Sally with me. If I make mistakes she'll correct me.'

Sally jerked in her chair.

'You never mentioned that I was to adopt the role of guardian,' she protested.

'You're my companion, really, but at the same time you'll be my champion as well as my adviser.'

'That's a whole lot of responsibility,' laughed Mrs Rotherham, then she added confidently, 'But you'll do very well, Sally, for you always were more than ordinarily equipped with wisdom and foresight.'

CHAPTER TWO

SALLY knew she would never forget the first meeting with Kort Lander. Not only was he as impersonal and aloof as some exalted royal personage, but he was almost openly hostile towards Sally.

Having been introduced by his brother who on meeting Nicole had been filled with admiration for her, Kort had seemed to be more interested in Sally than in the girl whom his brother wanted to marry. His hand had hurt as he clasped hers, his eyes had pierced and examined, critical and cold.

'I trust you had a good journey?' he said, and his eyes did then flicker to Nicole, and he frowned, and seemed as if he considered his brother to be out of his mind even to have opened up a correspondence with her. She was too young, he was thinking. Sally guessed this at once. She was English and would not know the first thing about life in the remote Outback; she would never be able to stand it. Suddenly Sally made a mental vow that, if Nicole did happen to want to marry Ray, then this brother of his was not going to do anything to prevent the marriage. He would if he could, she surmised, herself feeling small and inadequate—and uncomfortably inferior. What Nicole was feeling Sally could not guess, but, glancing at her, she could see at once that she was uneasy, to say the least.

'We've had a most pleasant journey,' answered Sally, not quite sure to whom the question was directed. 'The flight here was interesting, as neither

Nicole nor I had ever been in a small aeroplane before.'

'We who live in these remote places usually have our own private planes,' he said. And then, 'Ray, see to the comfort of your guests. I have work to do.' He strode away, in the direction of a paddock in which several beautiful horses grazed.

'They're being broken,' explained Ray, noticing Sally's interest. 'They're wild—brumbies we call them —and we caught them with the intention of using them on the station.' He seemed ill at ease, and no wonder, thought Sally. His brother's lack of hospitality must without doubt have made him feel uncomfortable.

A lubra appeared as they entered the oak-panelled hall, and Ray gave her instructions. She nodded all the while, taking no notice of him but interestedly examining each girl in turn. She knew what was required of her and Sally realized that Ray was talking for talking's sake only. He seemed totally lacking in confidence, and Sally wondered if already he was having second thoughts about the wisdom of his move in bringing Nicole here.

The girls eventually found themselves in their respective rooms—elegant rooms furnished with taste and at no thought for cost. Sally had scarcely begun to unpack when, hearing a knock on her door, she called, 'come in,' and smiled at her foster-sister.

'What is it?' she asked gently. 'Don't look so harassed. The man can't eat you.'

'Isn't he awful, Sally? Oh, but I'm glad you're with me! If you weren't I'm afraid he would overpower me within hours, and I'd be wanting to go home.' She was speaking in jerky tones and Sally guessed that she was almost in tears. Leaving what she was doing, she moved over to her and, putting an arm around her waist, led her to the window.

'Take a look out there, Nicole. Isn't it marvellous? The mountains, changing colour as the sun goes down; the vast spinifex plains, and the creek over there. It'll be a delight when after the rains its water sparkles and dances over the boulders. And look at those hills, with the stockriders looking after the cattle. Don't you feel that, even if you decide you don't want to stay, it'll all have been worth it? To see another continent—oh, I myself feel very privileged and fortunate!'

Nicole touched her hand.

'You always appreciate what's there, don't you, Sally? You're so different from anyone else I know.' Nicole looked at her, her pretty face deeply troubled. 'We didn't have a very good reception from Kort, and I'm feeling so far away from home as well....' She bit her lip, because it was trembling. 'Was I too impulsive, do you think, in deciding to accept Ray's offer to come over here?'

Sally shook her head.

'It's all strange, pet, and you're tired too, after the long journey——'

'But you must be tired, as well.'

'I suppose I shall feel it later. But for the present I'm too excited by it all. I hope I'm not appearing callous, or anything like that?' Sally added rather contritely.

'Callous! You!' Nicole actually gave a little laugh at this idea. 'You're the kindest person I know, and that's why I was so upset by the way Kort treated you.'

'Me?'

'He seemed more hostile to you than he was to me, I thought.'

So Nicole had noticed it too. Sally had hoped this circumstance would have escaped her.

'Never mind about Kort Lander,' she said after a space. 'Ray's nice, and I'm sure that you're going to get along famously with him.'

Nicole seemed to be endeavouring to read Sally's expression as she said, very quietly,

'But you don't feel I should marry him?'

Sally frowned.

'That's a strange question, Nicole. I can't possibly pass an opinion on Ray yet. I've already said he's nice —in fact, I would say he was charming. But as the whole object of this visit is to discover whether or not you and he are suited to be married, then we mustn't begin making hasty assessments, must we?'

'We've made a hasty assessment of Kort's character, though.'

'I haven't, Nicole. True, he was abrupt almost to the point of rudeness. But he did say he had work to do, and as we've no reason for disputing this, we can't say whether or not it was merely an excuse to get away from us, can we?'

'No, you're quite right.' Wistfully Nicole glanced around. 'I wish we were sharing a bedroom,' she said. 'Mine's lovely, but it's so big—and I shall feel quite lost in that great bed.'

'No such thing, love. It's because it's strange, and because you've never been away before without Mum. Buck up, Nicole; you'll feel better in a day or two, you'll see.'

Actually Nicole felt better by that evening when,

after an excellent dinner of roast lamb and home-grown vegetables, followed by strawberry flan and cream, Ray asked her to stroll with him outside in the gardens. She was all smiles, deliberately avoiding the half-contemptuous glance of Kort as he watched her walk beside Ray and disappear into the dimness of the gardens.

Sally was left with Kort, sitting on the verandah, her empty coffee cup in front of her on the rattan table.

He glanced from the two indistinct shadows of Ray and Nicole, to Sally, his eyes coldly indifferent as they flashed, in a perfunctory manner, over her face. She found herself colouring, more with anger than embarrassment. What an insufferable man he was, this arrogant grazier from the Outback, this man who believed he should dictate to his young brother, planning his life.

Sally wondered when he would break the silence. She herself felt awkward and would have said something—anything—in order to end this grim and intense quietness which existed, but she remained stubbornly silent, just to force him to speak. And at length he looked at her, bringing his attention from the dark shadows on the hillside, the figures of his stockriders and the vast herd of cattle among which they roamed, and he said, in his slow Australian drawl,

'This girl, Nicole—she isn't going to fit in here. I expect you've already concluded this?'

Sally frowned.

'What makes you say a thing like that? In the first place none of us has had time to pass an opinion; and in the second place it's not my conclusions which will count in the end. Nicole will make up her own mind.'

Kort's blue eyes glinted. She guessed that his anger had risen owing to the short and crisp tones in which she had answered him.

'Nicole will make up her own mind, you say? I thought your role was that of adviser?'

'In a way I suppose it is,' she had to own. 'Nicole's a sensible girl and she's already intimated her desire for me to advise her.'

Kort said nothing for a space, his attention having returned to the shadows away in the distance where the immensity of the spinifex plains lay in tranquil silence and solitude, with the vague outline of the MacDonnell Ranges rising beyond them.

'Adviser,' repeated Kort Lander eventually, his brow creased in thought. 'And nursemaid, eh?' he added with a hint of cynical amusement.

Sally bristled. What was the man trying to do?— make her so angry that she would subject him to an unladylike show of temper? He had another think coming! Cold as ice she would be, and throwing in sarcasm and arrogance for good measure—but temper? No! He would never succeed in arousing her to that extent, at least, not outwardly. Inside, she was already smouldering, but there was nothing in her calm gaze to reveal this.

'Nicole isn't in need of a nursemaid, Mr Lander,' she said at last.

'How long has she been left school? My brother tells me the pen-friendship began while she was still at school.'

'Yes, it did. She's been left school only a few weeks.' Sally spoke reluctantly, aware that it must seem, to any man of Kort Lander's age and experience, that Nicole was a mere child. The sudden curve

27

of his mouth revealed this to be true, and his words also proved her assumption to be correct.

'A schoolgirl as wife to a man who has to run a vast cattle station? And an English girl too, who has no experience of the austerity of life out here, in the Outback? The whole idea's so absurd that my brother must eventually realize his mistake in bringing this girl out from England.'

'You don't appear to be at all concerned with Nicole's feelings,' said Sally curtly.

'Her feelings don't matter very much,' he returned indifferently. 'She's young; she isn't in love with my brother. She hasn't lost anything by coming here—in fact, she's managed to get herself a free trip, so she's nothing to complain about, has she?'

'It doesn't seem to have occurred to you that there might be something deep between Nicole and Ray——'

'You're suggesting they fell in love by post?' Kort gave a short, cynical laugh that grated on Sally's ears. 'Miss Prentice, I haven't known you very long, but I'd wager you'd be the first to scoff at the idea of falling in love by post.'

She had to own that this was correct; she had already voiced this opinion to her foster-mother. However, Sally had no intention of giving away a point to this arrogant grazier, so she said, in her calm and quiet tones,

'It's possible that they've fallen in love, Mr Lander.'

His mouth twisted in a sneer of derision.

'So you're not willing to be honest? Strange, since I did gain the impression that you were a thoroughly frank and honest person.'

She flushed, and averted her head.

'If that's supposed to be a compliment——' she began when he immediately interrupted her with,

'It was the voicing of an impression. I never extend compliments to females; they've an inflated opinion of themselves already.'

She said tartly,

'It's very plain that you dislike my sex, Mr Lander!'

'I'm indifferent to them, Miss Prentice.'

'In that case,' she returned, adopting a tone of acid sweetness, 'you ought not to be taking such an interest in Nicole.'

'My interest lies mainly with my brother. If he's to be my heir then he must have a wife who'll enhance his prestige, not detract from it.'

Sally had to count ten very slowly. For otherwise her resolve of a few moments ago would have been blown sky-high!

'As you don't know my foster-sister, it's mere arrogance on your part to say that she could detract from your brother's prestige.'

Kort looked at her; she had the impression that he had been diverted by the word foster-sister. She found herself waiting for him to question her, but if such had been his intention he changed his mind.

'Perhaps you don't fully understand the position here, Miss Prentice,' he said at length. 'We who own vast estates are——'

'I do understand the position here,' she broke in, fully aware that the interruption was rude, but at the same time impelled to let him know that she was not quite so ignorant as he assumed her to be. 'You graziers own estates which are sometimes as large as a country. You're almost self-supporting. You have your

29

own villages, your own schools and shops and hospitals. This is all very necessary on a cattle station of such vast proportions. You're called the squatocracy and your fellow members are just as aware of their own importance as you are——' She stopped, because his eyebrows had shot up, and his eyes had taken on a look of cold steel. 'Perhaps,' she said, injecting a note of apology into her voice, 'that was not very well put——'

'It was extremely badly put,' he cut in, his drawl not so slow now, and its edge was knife-sharp. 'However, it would appear you have done your homework before coming here and you have the picture generally correct. You will realize, then, that my brother will be one of the most important members of our society— having the ownership not only of his own ranch, Walleroo Creek, but of mine too. Therefore, it's imperative that Ray's wife be accepted in our society.' Here he paused, his eyes resting on Sally's face for a long moment before he added, his voice now slow and deliberate, 'In my opinion your foster-sister is totally unfitted to be Ray's wife.'

Sally's first impulse was to shoot back some acid retort, deriding Kort for jumping to conclusions. But suddenly it was borne in upon her that Kort did have a point—a strong point. Nicole at seventeen was, as he had implied, a mere child; and she was English. These autocratic Outback men usually married Australian women—in many cases daughters of other graziers— and it was conceivable that they would not take kindly to a very young girl from another country. However, as there was not the remotest possibility of Ray's inheriting Grey River Downs for some considerable time to come, it did seem that Kort Lander was running well ahead of himself. This she mentioned, her eyes automatically taking in his healthy tan, his clear skin whose only lines were those which fanned out—most attractively, she owned, but grudgingly—from the corners of his eyes, lines caused, surmised Sally, by the continual narrowing of his eyes against the fierce rays of the Australian sun. She noted his broad shoulders, the perfect physique of his lithe and sinewed body, the deceptive slenderness of his brown hands —hands that might have belonged to a surgeon, she thought, while at the same time vaguely trying to assess their strength.

'It's quite true that I'm not expecting to die in the near future,' Kort was saying, and she was sure there was an edge of humour in his voice. 'However, one can't be sure of anything where heart and lungs are concerned. We're all vulnerable to accident or to disease. I must plan for the future in any case and, as I've said, Nicole is not the wife for Ray.'

Sally was frowning as again she was admitting to Kort's having a point.

'You're being ungenerous,' she told him at last. 'Nicole is young, but as I've already said, she's a most sensible girl. She could have come here alone, remember. She hadn't thought of doing so simply because she knew her mother would be out of her mind with worry. That was why I came with her....' She allowed her voice to trail away to silence as she saw Kort lift a hand to his mouth to hide a yawn. Anger flared within her at this manifestation of his being bored with what she was saying. She added coldly, 'I see that all this is of no interest to you, Mr Lander!'

He cast her a slow observant glance.

'Have I done something to arouse your temper?' he

inquired with maddening calm which held the merest trace of amusement.

She waited, gathering her own composure, so that when she did speak her voice was steady, and even friendly, in a casual kind of way.

'Not at all, Mr Lander. How could you have gained such an impression?'

He looked at her, perceptively.

'It would seem,' he drawled, 'that you and I are to be enemies, Miss Prentice.'

She held his stare.

'If so, Mr Lander, it will be of your choosing. I myself am not a quarrelsome person, as Nicole will be only too willing to tell you. I can't recall ever having felt any real enmity towards anyone in the whole of my life.' She was remembering what Joyce had said about her being able to get along with anyone. This was true; in all modesty Sally had to give herself credit for the ability to bear with the faults of others, and even to excuse them in certain circumstances. She always maintained that she herself had faults—it could not be otherwise. And as people bore with her faults, it was incumbent on her to bear with theirs. Besides, life was far more pleasant when people were friendly towards one another. However, it would seem that life was not going to be any bed of roses here, on Grey River Downs. On the contrary, life was going to be most unpleasant—unless she could avoid this man's company. This she decided to do if it was at all possible, and as the days went by and she became familiar with the routine of a great cattle station such as this one, she became a little easier in her mind, for Kort went off every morning, riding a superb chestnut gelding, and he was not seen again until about an hour before dinner was served.

Nicole, flushed and radiant, came riding towards Sally, then as she reached her she dismounted and handed the reins to the rouseabout who immediately took the horse to the paddock. Sally was by the gate leading to another, empty paddock in which one of the stockriders had been breaking a brumbie. The horse put up a tremendous resistance and now he had been taken to even yet another enclosure where he would rest until the following day, grazing the lush grass and becoming used to his new surroundings.

'Oh, but I've had a wonderful ride with Ray!' Nicole was happy and it showed. Sally was troubled, but it didn't show. She smiled and said,

'Where's Ray now?'

'Gone off to join the stockmen. Sally ... do you like him?'

'Of course,' was Sally's instant reply. 'Who wouldn't like him?'

'I'm glad! He's asked me again to marry him.'

Sally nodded her head.

'I knew he would.' She paused a moment. 'But it's still early days, Nicole,' she reminded her.

'We've been here for over a week.'

A swift smile touched Sally's lips.

'A week's nothing, my love.'

'We've been together a great deal, though.'

'That,' said Sally with a wry grimace, 'is something which surprises me immensely. I'm beginning to suspect Kort of some artful move or intention.'

Nicole frowned.

'I don't understand?'

'Kort's a stickler for hard work. Hasn't it struck you as odd that he allows his brother to spend so much time with you?'

Nicole's chin lifted. It struck Sally that her foster-sister possessed a growing strength of character which could in the end surprise the man who was treating her with such disdain.

'Ray's his own boss, Sally. This we tend to forget. He owns the estate adjoining this one, and lives here, with his brother, only because he's done so all his life. He was a mere child when his father died and it was natural that he should stay here, at Grey River Downs, under the care and guardianship of his elder brother. But he can, at any time he wants, remove himself to his own property.'

'Then why doesn't he?' asked Sally, puzzled. 'Why does he stay here to be ordered about by Kort?'

'Kort doesn't actually give him orders,' returned Nicole, her eyes scanning the wide plains, searching for Ray among the mob of cattle grazing so peacefully there.

'But Kort does tend to run his life for him,' argued Sally. 'The very fact that he wants to choose a wife for Ray is proof and enough of that.'

Nicole nodded her head.

'I agree to a point. But as for the reason why Ray doesn't take up residence at his own property—it's just that, before I came into the picture, the position suited Ray. He didn't have any desire to cut himself off from Kort, and it would be cutting himself off, in a way, because Walleroo Creek's over a hundred miles from here.'

'So far?' Sally knew of course that Ray's property must be some considerable distance from the homestead of Grey River Downs, but she had not expected the distance to be as great as a hundred miles.

'Yes, so you can see why Ray had no desire to go and live there, all on his own, can't you?'

'Yes, it's understandable.'

'If we marry, though, it'll be different. We'll naturally want to live in our own home rather than in Kort's.'

'Has Ray not suggested taking you to see Walleroo Creek?'

'He has, yes, but I must admit, Sally, that he's most reluctant to upset his brother.'

'Upset Kort?' Sally looked askance at her foster-sister. 'Why should Kort be upset by Ray's taking you to see his homestead?'

Nicole shook her head, and her gaiety seemed to fade, replaced by a tinge of anxiety.

'Ray seems cautious—oh, I can't really explain his attitude towards Kort, Sally. But I get the impression that Ray's afraid of hurting his brother.'

'Hurting!' scoffed Sally, shaking her head. 'That one could never be hurt—not mentally, that is!'

'So I believed, and said so to Ray. But—and you'll not believe this, Sally—Kort was once in love ... and she let him down. Ray says it took him a very long time to get over it.'

Amazed by this unexpected piece of information, Sally could only stare, speechless for a moment or two.

'It doesn't seem possible!' she exclaimed. 'Kort Lander—in love!' Vigorously she shook her head. 'I can't take that in, Nicole. I'm sorry.'

'It's true, I tell you!'

'He might have had a girl-friend——'

'They were engaged. She was the daughter of a wealthy grazier.'

'So it was a business arrangement,' decided Sally. 'Just like Kort to want to enlarge his property. I expect it was disappointment rather than hurt which he suffered.'

'Ray is of the opinion that he was broken-hearted.'

Sally laughed; she could not help it. Kort Lander broken-hearted! It was too incredible even to be considered.

'When did all this happen?' she asked.

'When Ray was ten.'

'And Kort twenty-one,' mused Sally. 'Twelve years ago.' She paused, half inclined now to consider the possibility of Kort's having been in love. Calf love, it could have been, and perhaps the disappointment was responsible for his present attitude towards women.

'Yes, twelve years ago,' repeated Nicole. 'It's a long time, isn't it?'

'A very long time. What happened to this girl who let him down?'

'She married a wealthy businessman she met in Sydney when she went there on a visit to her grandmother.'

'She lives in Sydney now?'

'At present, yes. But Ray says that a friend of his who's in a bank there has written to him recently to say that this woman's husband has died and she's considering selling up her luxury home and returning to her father's estate here in the Outback.'

Sally gave a grimace.

'So our friend Kort might just get married after all?'

Nicole shook her head.

36

'Ray says there isn't a hope. Kort's no time at all for women now. He's self-sufficient; his whole life is this station.'

'It's been in the family for a long time?'

'Yes; his great-grandfather came here as a pioneer, then sent for his fiancée. It was tough in those days, Sally. You must get Ray to talk about it some time.'

'I will. It should make interesting listening.'

'Of course,' suggested Nicole with a flash of mischief which was familiar to Sally, 'you could make an attempt to bring out his brother.'

'Now why that particular tone of voice?' Sally wanted to know.

'Because it's more than plain that you and Kort are sworn enemies.'

'It's more than plain?' Sally raised her brows. 'I hadn't thought anyone had noticed.'

'We've all noticed.'

'All?'

'Ray and me and the two stockriders, Tyler and Ruff.'

'I see. . . .' Did it matter? Sally shrugged inwardly. It was a bit late now to worry about such things.

But that evening at dinner she naturally watched the expressions of the others, especially those of the two stockmen. Ruff, red-haired and tough as old leather, was always deep in thought, or so it seemed. Having come to Grey River Downs over thirty years ago as a rouseabout, he was now a valued stockrider. He could do many other things besides looking after cattle, though. He was an expert at breaking horses, at throwing a bull, at shooting a marauding dingo. He did odd jobs about the homestead, or repairs to sheds or equipment. The runway constructed for Kort's private aeroplane was supervised by Ruff during the time it was being laid down.

Catching Sally's eye, he seemed puzzled by her attention, and after offering her a thin smile he concentrated on his food. Tyler, on the other hand, slanted many a glance from Sally to the boss, and his lips would purse, or a slight frown would pucker his bushy brow. As toughened as his friend, Ruff, he was a few years younger, and a few inches shorter. His hair was grey, as was Ruff's, but Tyler's was thick and curly while that of Ruff was sparse on top and long and straight at the sides. Both men were immaculately clean when they appeared at the dinner table each evening, their shirts being freshly washed and ironed, this being done by the two lubras who worked in the house. Another lubra, the cook, held a somewhat higher, more important position, and she was always ready to make this evident.

'I don't have anything to do with the ordinary chores,' she had told Sally with dignity when by mistake Sally had asked her to take a duster to her bedroom, as it had not been touched for three days. 'Susannah will do it for you, miss.'

Susannah had been faintly piqued.

'Elsa thinks she is high-and-mighty around here!' And this was supplemented by Augusta's,

'She has one big head!'

However, all three lubras got along quite well together, with each usually keeping to her own duties. Elsa had the hardest task, having to cook masses of mutton every morning for the men's breakfast—and this was not only for the two who lived in, but for those who lived in the nearby settlement of bungalows. Some of the stockriders were married, of course, but for those who were single, and sharing a bungalow with one or two others, there was always food to be had in the kitchen. This did not include dinner, a meal which the men would cook for themselves in their bungalows or, if they happened to be a long way from home, they would manage with billy tea and damper, or perhaps tinned beef if they happened to have this with them.

'You're miles away, Sally!' This from Nicole, who had been watching her foster-sister for the past two or three minutes. 'What are you thinking about?'

Sally looked at her and smiled.

'It was nothing of interest, Nicole,' she answered, aware of Kort's momentary interest as he waited for her reply. Immaculate in an off-white tropical suit of finest linen, he looked almost regal now—the perfect example of a noble member of the squatocracy. And she supposed that he had every right to adopt that superior air, when he owned an estate of ten thousand or so square miles.

Aware of her interest he glanced her way again, and his brows lifted a fraction, a gesture which always annoyed her since it savoured of arrogance in its worst form. It was meant to make her feel small, inferior, and as always she was impelled to do battle with him.

'Was there something you wanted to ask me?' she inquired, adopting that tone of acid sweetness to which he was fast becoming used.

'Not that I know of,' with dignity. 'What makes you ask?'

'The way you lifted your eyebrows,' she rejoined, looking directly at him, a glint in her gaze. 'It was a gesture of interrogation, I thought.'

'I'm afraid I can't help what you think, Miss

Prentice. If you must read your own meaning into any-thing I do, then that's entirely your own affair.'

Snubbed, and in front of all these people! Sally blushed, much to her chagrin, and in this moment she felt she hated the man for the humiliation he was causing her. Ray was appalled; it showed in the start he had given and now in the look he was directing at his brother from the opposite end of the table. Nicole had made a low exclamation which sounded like, 'O-oh. . . .' while both Ruff and Tyler had stopped eating, each with his knife and fork poised in mid-air. Kort looked around, his cool glance passing from one to another until he had circled the entire table. Sally, re-fusing to meet his eye, averted her head. She heard Kort's voice, abrupt and demanding, telling Elsa to serve him with more vegetables.

A silence prevailed for a time after this, but even-tually polite conversation began to flow again. Ray was talking about a bull that had gone wild and taken off from the herd.

'Will you get it back?' asked Nicole.

'Perhaps, but it's unlikely.'

Nicole shivered.

'I hope I won't meet it when I'm out there in the wilds!'

Kort's attention was instantly arrested.

'You'll not be out there in the wilds,' he said in his soft and rich Australian drawl. 'At least, not alone.'

Nicole's eyes opened wide.

'I love walking,' she said. 'I've already been for a long tramp. And yesterday Sally came with me. We must have gone for miles, mustn't we?' She turned to Sally, who nodded her head.

'Yes, and it was wonderful.'

'Don't do it again.' Kort's voice was abrupt. He had actually given an order, Sally realized—and her temper flared at once. However, unwilling to begin an argument before all these witnesses, she saved what she had to say until later, when once again she found herself alone on the verandah with the boss of Grey River Downs.

'About our walking in the countryside,' she began as soon as the young couple were out of earshot, 'I see no reason for our not doing so.'

'There's a very good reason, Miss Prentice. You're sure to get lost.'

'Sure?' She gave a short laugh. 'Nonsense!'

His blue eyes glinted, like steel newly sharpened.

'You'll do as I suggest, and not take long walks out over the plains.'

'As you suggest, Mr Lander?' she murmured, 'or as you order?'

Kort showed her a tense, unsmiling countenance.

'Order it is, then,' he returned and, rising from his chair, he politely excused himself and walked away, leaving Sally sitting there, alone on the verandah, and inwardly squirming under the humiliating knowledge that she had once again been snubbed by the arrogant and high-handed boss of Grey River Downs cattle station.

CHAPTER THREE

SHE made no move, but continued to sit in the quiet of the evening, her nostrils assailed by the elusive, intangible scent of herbs as it came over the endless spinifex plains, borne on the zephyr of a breeze drifting out from the mountains. She was thoughtful, and a little afraid for Nicole, who appeared to be so happy, and so settled as regarded her future. But always Sally was reminded of the small amount of time the couple had had. It was not enough even for them to get to know one another, much less to discover whether or not they were suited in the way that married people should be suited.

Then there loomed so starkly the shadow of Kort's dislike not only of Nicole but of women in general. He appeared to have been determined right from the start to adopt an antagonistic manner towards Sally. With Nicole his manner might have been that of an impatient old uncle towards an errant niece. He could find nothing at all to recommend her; he saw nothing attractive in her childlike prettiness, or in her apparent naïveté which sometimes was buried beneath a cover of pure common sense.

The young couple appeared from out of the shadows of a large clump of eucalypts and entered the garden proper. Hand in hand, they walked close together, a typical courting couple, Sally's foster-mother would say, could she have seen them now.

They saw her and came up on to the verandah.

'All alone, Sally?' Ray looked a trifle worried, she thought, staring up into his young and handsome face. His mouth, wide and with none of the' firmness portrayed in that of his brother, was full and compassionate, his chin well shaped but not outthrust like Kort's. In fact, mused Sally, the two men were very different in appearance, even though their eyes were the same colour and so was their hair.

'I don't mind being alone, Ray,' she assured him with a smile. 'It's rather wonderful sitting here, in such a peaceful setting. Just look at the moonlight on the mountains! Look how it sharpens the lines of their summits.'

'Imagine your appreciating things like that!' Ray spoke in wondering tones, his eyes moving from Sally's beautiful face to the moonlit crests she was indicating. 'Usually tourists don't even notice.'

'But I'm not a tourist,' she pointed out.

'Well, no, not exactly. Nevertheless, I'm afraid I have considered you as a tourist, Sally, because of course you're here only on a short visit.'

'Short?' she repeated, nerves tingling.

'We're getting married, Sally.' It was Nicole who spoke, in tones that held a trace of apology. 'We're in love and it's no use waiting.'

Sally's eyes went to Ray. He nodded in answer to her unspoken request for confirmation, but he was not happy. . . .

She said, after a small silence,

'Ray . . . would you care to talk with me alone?'

Strangely, Nicole made no objection, but remained silent while Ray, taking a few seconds to make up his mind, stood fidgeting with his hands.

'Yes, I would,' he decided all at once. 'Nicole

darling, you don't mind? You did say, earlier on, that Sally might want to have a talk with me, remember?'

Nicole smiled lovingly at him.

'There's no need to make excuses, Ray. Talk to Sally by all means. I'm tired anyway, so I'll say good night to you both.'

'Good night, pet,' from Sally. 'Sleep well.'

Ray went into the room with her; they were there a few minutes and then Ray reappeared and sat down opposite to Sally. He seemed lost for words and it was Sally who spoke first.

'What is it, Ray? I know we haven't known one another very long, but the circumstances being what they are it would seem there's a need for you to confide in me.'

'You're worried about Nicole?'

'Not entirely. But you must remember that her mother expects me to see that she's doing the right thing.'

Ray nodded his head.

'You say not entirely. Does that mean that you believe I'll make Nicole a good husband?'

Sally hesitated, recalling things she had read about the average Australian man.

'In England,' she ventured cautiously, 'the women are considered equals by the men.'

He frowned suddenly.

'But that's also the case here.'

'I'm not so sure, Ray. From what I've read women are still in an inferior position. For example, I've read somewhere lately that a woman dare not speak to another man for fear of her husband having a quarrel with her once he gets her home.' It was partly a question and Ray said that in all honesty he had to

44

agree that Australian men were exceedingly jealous where the relationship between their wives and other men were concerned.

'It's true that women have to be careful,' he ended, looking apologetically at her.

'A most uncomfortable state of affairs, surely?'

'You mean that if you were married you'd like to talk to other men?'

'Decidedly I would! I can't imagine myself having to remain dumb just because of fear of my husband's wrath——' Sally broke off, turning swiftly as she became aware of another presence. Kort was standing in the open window behind the verandah, the shade of a cynical smile hovering about his lips.

Ray spoke, informing him that he and Sally were having a private talk.

'So I've realized,' was Kort's cool rejoinder as he stepped from the aperture on to the verandah and took possession of a chair. 'You were discussing the jealous traits of the Australian man, Miss Prentice?'

'It's a private talk, Kort,' repeated Ray. 'Sally and I were talking about Nicole and me.'

'And Miss Prentice pointed out that, if you and Nicole married, Nicole should be free to flirt with other men——'

'I pointed out no such thing!' flashed Sally, forgetting her firm resolve not to show Kort her temper. 'How dare you eavesdrop, then twist my words!'

'My listening was not deliberate, I assure you. I happened to enter the room there and heard what Ray was saying.' His glance went to his brother. 'Am I to understand that your decision is made, and that you're intending to marry this English girl without further delay?'

Ray licked his dry lips.

'Yes—er—yes, that's s-so, Kort.'

'I see. . . .' A faint sigh escaped him, but otherwise he appeared unmoved by the information he had been given. 'What have you to say about it?' He looked at Sally, his glance perfunctory and fleeting.

'To be quite honest, I haven't had time to think seriously about it.'

'Does Nicole have to have your approval?'

'Certainly not! However, as I've just mentioned to Ray, I did promise Nicole's mother that I'd try to influence her into doing the right thing.'

'By that,' remarked Kort with a sort of impersonal formality, 'you mean you'd try to guide her into making the right decision?'

'That's what I said,' she almost snapped. 'You're splitting hairs, Mr Lander.'

Kort ignored that and once again Sally felt that she had received a snub. Pompous creature! She almost wished that Nicole was married already, so that she, Sally, would be free to leave Grey River Downs and never have to come into contact with its lofty-minded boss again.

'In your opinion, Miss Prentice,' said Kort, 'is Nicole ready for marriage?'

She started at the question, as it was put without the usual animosity. In fact, it was a logical question which she herself could have put to Nicole.

'I'm not sure,' she was honest enough to admit. 'In any case, both she and Ray ought to get to know one another better before they rush into so serious a thing as marriage.'

The solemnity of her words, the anxiety in her lovely eyes, the slight quivering of her lips . . . all these

46

seemed to have some effect on the man sitting there in the chair. He looked at her hard and long, his brow furrowed in thought.

'Ray,' he said at length, 'what are your ideas about Nicole's youth?'

'I know she's young, Kort, but she's a most sensible girl. She'll be inexperienced, but she's willing to learn.'

A sneer seemed to come to Kort Lander's lips.

'Youthful optimism,' he commented sarcastically. 'How can you be so sure that she's willing to learn?'

'She told me so.'

'And you believed her?'

'Nicole doesn't tell lies, Mr Lander!' snapped Sally before Ray could speak. 'If she says she's willing to learn then you can be sure she means it!'

The deep blue eyes glinted dangerously. It was plain that the arrogant boss of Grey River Downs was not used to being spoken to in this manner.

'You can't prevent our marriage,' put in Ray swiftly, obviously deciding to intervene before his brother and Sally became more deeply involved in the animosity which was fast developing between them.

Kort made no response to this and Sally wondered if he were furious at having to admit that what Ray said was correct: he had no authority at all over his brother's actions and therefore he could do nothing to prevent an early marriage between him and Nicole.

As for Sally's own reaction to the idea of an early marriage—she meant it when she expressed the opinion that the couple should wait awhile so that they could get to know one another a little better.

Kort rose from the chair; she sensed his inner anger now, for his lips were tight and his jaw flexed. Never had she seen a more formidable face than Kort's at this moment.

'As you say,' he murmured, looking directly at his brother, 'I can't prevent your marriage. However, I can advise—and my advice is to wait, as Miss Prentice has said.' And with that he was gone, leaving Sally and Ray to continue the discussion. Ray was miserable; he heaved a great sigh and looked imploringly at Sally.

'What must I do?' he asked, and to her surprise there was something akin to desperation in his voice.

'Wait, as your brother advises.'

'You don't understand, Sally. No one does!' He was wringing his hands, but he scarcely knew it. 'You see, the girl Kort wants me to marry is returning to her home in a fortnight's time. Before she went away—she's been in Brisbane with her father's sister —I saw her and promised to give her my answer when she came back.'

'You——!' Sally stared at him. 'I don't understand, Ray. Has there been a sort of—engagement between you and this girl?'

'No, nothing like that. But we've had an understanding—if you know what I mean, since we were young. It was all arranged between Kort and Dora's father. Dora is as old as I, and thoroughly at home in the Outback. She's confident and poised; she belongs to everything—like the riding club we have. She's used to acting as hostess because her mother died when she was only sixteen. In fact, she has everything which Nicole lacks—and on top of all that she's an Australian.'

'What did you have against marrying her?'

'Nothing, to be honest. It was merely rebellion at

48

the idea of having Kort choose my wife for me.'

'I thought it was!'

'What do you mean?'

'When I knew you'd proposed to Nicole I concluded at once that it was an act of rebellion, because Nicole had said that your brother wanted you to marry a girl of his choosing.'

'I really care for Nicole, though,' he said, but something in his tone brought an alertness to Sally's expression.

'Forgive me, Ray, but you don't sound very convincing.'

He bit his lip.

'I'm beginning to love Nicole.'

'I see. But as yet you don't know your own mind?'

'Well. . . .'

'Don't prevaricate, Ray,' she broke in sternly. 'Nicole's happiness means a lot to me; it means a lot to her mother as well. Unless you can convince me that you really love her then there'll be no marriage. I shan't tell her the content of this conversation, not for the present, that is. But make no mistake, Ray, I'm not standing by and watching you make use of her.'

'I wouldn't do that, Sally!'

She looked squarely at him.

'I'm not convinced. By your own admission you've said that your act in proposing to Nicole was one of rebellion against your brother. You've also admitted that you have nothing against this girl Dora.' Sally paused. 'Be honest, Ray, do you think any more of Nicole than you do of Dora?'

He shook his head, unable for the moment to phrase an answer, and Sally's eyes narrowed. How glad she was that she had agreed to come here with

Nicole! The child could very well have ruined her life.

'I don't know,' owned Ray at last, still shaking his head. 'I certainly don't have any love for Dora, but I must admit I like her a lot.'

'And Nicole?' said Sally in terse and even tones.

'I have a strong affection for her—yes, truly I do!' The last four words were added vehemently as he saw the look of cynicism that had entered Sally's eyes.

'You've led her to believe you're in love with her. You ought not to have done it, but I suppose you know that without my telling you?'

'Yes. And I was deeply troubled by my insincerity.'

'I sensed that you were troubled when you came to me with Nicole a short while ago. However, I believe you'll be sincere with her in future——'

'But what am I to do about the proposal I've made to her?'

'Just tell her what both your brother and I advise. I know Nicole a lot better than you do, Ray, and I'm fairly certain that she'll be reasonable and take the advice offered by those older and wiser than herself.'

He nodded in agreement, but brought forward the question of Dora again.

'I promised to give her my answer,' he repeated. 'What can I say to her?'

'You can't be in any worse position than if you were engaged to Nicole,' pointed out Sally reasonably. 'I can't understand just what you had in mind when you sent for my foster-sister to come over here.'

'I hoped we'd be married before Dora got back.'

'So you were intending to do the dirty on Dora—to put the matter in its crudest terms.'

Ray licked his lips.

'I know it must sound absurd to you, Sally, but somehow I felt it would simplify matters if I was already married to someone else.'

She said crisply,

'You're quite right when you say it must sound absurd. I've never come across anything quite so absurd in my life!' She looked at him, waiting for some comment, but none came. 'You were intending to treat this girl in exactly the same way your brother was once treated, it would seem?' Only then did it dawn on Sally that Ray might have told Nicole about that affair in confidence, not expecting her to repeat it to anyone else. However, as he made no protest she saw that it was all right.

'I thought that Dora would just cut me out of her life for ever,' he said unhappily.

'You'd have to meet her some time, surely?'

'Of course—at all the shed dances we have, and film shows and the like. We also have race meetings—— Oh, yes, I'd have had to meet her fairly often.'

'You weren't concerned with the embarrassment you would be bringing upon you both?'

He shrugged; Sally realized that he was tired of her persistence in probing like this.

'I myself would have been embarrassed, but Dora wouldn't. You see, the idea of giving her an answer was mine alone. No one else knows about it.'

'I'm puzzled as to just how the situation came about?'

He flushed, and hesitated a long while before making the confession that there had been a petting session and, carried away, he had made Dora the promise she had asked for.

'You see, we were at a party held by one of the

graziers. Dora and I wandered off, into the grounds, and we—kissed a little. She then reminded me that both her father and my brother expected us to marry. She pointed out all the advantages—mainly the joining of the estates, as she's her father's only child. We ought to be settling our futures, she said, and that was when I promised to make up my mind and give her an answer on her return. She was going away for three months and it seemed I had ages and ages in which to settle my future. But when a month passed so swiftly I became almost panic-stricken because I felt as if I were caught in a trap. It was then that I wanted to fight to release myself, and marriage to another girl seemed to be the answer.'

'It still sounds absurd to me,' returned Sally, not wanting to appear heartless but by now feeling totally out of patience with Ray. 'All you've done is to entangle yourself more deeply. You could have told this girl that your mind still was not made up; I daresay she'd have understood. She sounds a reasonably-minded young lady to me.'

'She is! Dora's a fine girl——' He stopped suddenly as if aware of his enthusiasm. 'Sally, I don't know where I'm up to with this business! It's all Kort's fault for being so set on my inheriting this place. It isn't as if I want it! I shall hate the responsibility. Walleroo Creek's about all I can manage——'

'You don't want this place?' interrupted Sally. 'Then why don't you tell your brother about your feelings?'

Ray shook his head at once.

'Impossible. He's set his heart on keeping the two estates intact. You don't know how these great landed graziers are. They want only to hold on to the lands which their forebears won through such hardships as drought and Abo raids, and many others.'

'You talk as though you yourself are not one of these graziers!'

'Of course I'm one of them. But my lands aren't nearly so extensive as some—and those of my brother are exceptional. Father didn't divide the estate into two equal parts. He gave the main estate to Kort and the much smaller estate brought to him by my mother was left to me.'

'And you're perfectly happy running this smaller estate?'

'I've not run it yet; Kort's done everything for me. When I marry I shall take over at once.'

'You feel confident of managing Walleroo Creek?'

'Yes, I do——' He stopped, and uttered a sigh of resignation. 'But I've got to have *this* place when anything happens to Kort. If only he'd get married and have a son! But that's wishful thinking and no mistake! He hasn't the remotest idea of ever getting married.'

'He dislikes women, from what I can gather,' said Sally reflectively, and Ray nodded in agreement.

'He has no time at all for them.'

Sally gave a sigh now, and shook her head.

'Well, if you must have Grey River Downs I suppose you must. However, that's not an urgent matter at present—nor will it be for some years to come unless something unforeseen happens to your brother.' Which was most unlikely, was her private conclusion, since there was no doubt in her mind that Kort Lander could take very good care of himself no matter how dangerous the position might be. 'The urgent matter,' she continued, 'is that of making up your mind which girl you want to marry. I suppose it has occurred to you that if you marry Dora then you're eventually going to own even more land?'

'Yes, but Dora's so capable. She herself could run her father's place without any trouble at all.'

'She must be capable,' rejoined Sally, her thoughts flying to Nicole and her total lack of experience.

'I think it's Nicole I want to marry——'

'*Thinking* isn't enough! Carry on as you're doing and if you don't fall in love with Nicole then I shall insist on her returning to England.'

'But——'

'That's my final word, Ray, so please don't argue with me!'

To Sally's relief Nicole was not averse to waiting a little while.

'I had an idea that both you and Kort would advise us to wait,' she confided to Sally. 'And although I'd like to get married soon I won't make a fuss. I'll be good and do as I'm told.'

'Bless you! Nicole, you're still a model daughter. Your mother's going to be very proud of you when I write and explain—or perhaps you'd prefer to do all the explaining yourself?'

Nicole said she would certainly write to her mother, but she preferred to leave the explaining to Sally.

'You'll do it better than I could,' she added, eyeing Sally affectionately. 'I'd only say something that would set Mum worrying, whereas you'll know how to be tactful.'

'I expect I shall merely tell her that you and Ray haven't yet been able to make up your minds and are waiting a little while in order to get to know one another better.' Sally looked at Nicole, saw the brightness in her eyes and the flush on her cheek. 'You're— you're very much in love with him, aren't you, Nicole?'

'Of course! Can't you tell?' She was smiling, and then the smile broke into a laugh. Sally swallowed hard, trying to dislodge the lump which had risen in her throat. She had never seen Nicole so happy and carefree ... but what was to come next? Was Nicole to return to England nursing a broken heart? Suddenly she was furious with Ray for his irresponsible and impetuous move in asking Nicole to marry him. But she was even more furious with Kort, for placing his brother in the position which precipitated that move. Unreasonable it might be, but Sally knew without any doubt at all that it would be Kort Lander who would come in for the cutting barb of her anger should Nicole suffer hurt over this affair.

The following morning Sally was up early, as usual, wakened by the avian bustle that went on in the tree outside her bedroom window. Not only was it the kookaburras with their raucous laughter, but the magpies too, those carollers of the dawn who always appeared to be experimenting with their vocal cords but never coming to any noticeable conclusion. Sally loved this morning chorus and she did not mind at all that she was brought rudely from her sleep by it.

She was in the garden, taking in the clear brittle air and sending it deep down into her lungs. There was no heady air like this where she came from, nor in the stuffy office where she had spent her working days. This was like nectar, she thought, and vaguely wondered how long it would take her to become accustomed once more to the confining walls of a city office.

She wandered about, interestedly absorbing the flowers and their lovely colours and scents, the birds around her, the more distant vista of spinifex plains and mountains. On the plains the cattle grazed, with the stockriders moving about among them. To the west, on the skyline, there suddenly appeared the beautiful form of a wild horse; it stopped its racing and stood, a magnificent creature, free as the wind, lord of the domain around it. Sally was unable to move from the spot, so fascinated was she by the sight—a sight she might never see again. Then suddenly she was conscious of someone behind her and she twisted about. A frown caught her brow as she watched the figure of Kort Lander approaching, his long easy strides eating up the distance. Sally's first impulse, as he drew closer, was to turn and make a hasty departure. But she immediately owned that this would not do at all. Such behaviour would only increase the antagonism which existed between the boss and herself.

So she managed a thin smile when presently he stopped before her. She was surprised that he should stop, but she concealed this as she said,

'Good morning, Mr Lander. Isn't it wonderful out here?' There was a wealth of appreciation in her voice, and Kort looked strangely at her. But if anything of a cordial nature leapt to his lips he immediately replaced it with,

'I'm surprised that you find it wonderful, Miss Prentice. From Nicole I've gathered that your home is in a town?'

'It is, yes; I'm forced to live within reasonable

56

distance of my place of work.' She paused, noting the rather bored expression on his face. 'But the fact of my living in a town doesn't preclude the possibility of my appreciating nature. It might interest you to know that I've always loved to walk in the countryside.' Her voice was curt and brittle, but if Kort noticed he chose to ignore it as he said offhandedly,

'Is Nicole a country-lover too?'

'She's both a country-lover and a home bird, Mr Lander.'

There was a cynical twist to his mouth as he asked,

'Just what are you trying to prove, Miss Prentice?'

'I'm wise enough not to try to prove anything to you,' she returned icily, wishing he would go and leave her to enjoy the lovely morning sun and the clear cool atmosphere which seemed to bring the mountains deceptively close.

'It would appear that already you're learning something about me,' he said evenly.

'What I'm learning is forced upon me. I have no desire voluntarily to learn anything about you at all.'

He cast her a narrowed look and she coloured faintly. Never had she been so rude to anyone in the whole of her life. But this pompous, self-opinionated creature brought out the very worst in her.

'Your manners leave a great deal to be desired,' he told her contemptuously. 'I'd have you remember you're a guest in my home.'

The barb found its mark, and it hurt! Sally glanced away, thoroughly ashamed of herself. And yet she could not bring herself to voice an apology; her pride prevented the adoption of humility.

'I shall remember in future,' she said, aware of the husky note in her tone but hoping it was unheard by

57

her companion.

'I very much doubt it,' returned Kort with irony. 'There appears to be something about me which arouses your hostility.'

'And something in me that arouses yours,' was her swift retort. And then she added, in a more sober tone, 'However, one way or another, this situation between Nicole and Ray should soon be resolved. I shall then be leaving and you'll no longer be plagued by my presence.'

To her utter surprise the glimmer of an amused smile came to his lips.

'Plagued is a rather strong word, Miss Prentice. I'll admit that your presence annoys me at times, but— plagued....' His lips actually twitched now. 'No, I couldn't in all honesty claim that you plague me.'

Sally looked uncertainly at him, still amazed by the change in him. Even his appearance was different, the half-smile transforming the hardness of his features to much softer lines. She guessed that he seldom spoke banteringly, and she did wonder if his reason for doing so now was in order to ease a situation that could have brought about a deepening of the rupture which undoubtedly existed between them.

Kort was speaking again; there was still a jesting edge to his voice as he asked if she had no comment to make.

'Is a comment necessary?' she countered, and instantly Kort grasped the fact of her being unable to find anything to say.

'I've floored you, have I, Miss Prentice?' He was looking into her eyes, those most attractive slanting blue eyes which so many people had admired. Then his gaze moved, to rest on her mouth, wide and

58

generous, and compassionate. It was a strange moment, with a tenseness in the air. Sally felt uncomfortable under his examination and yet, to her amazement, she knew a little access of pleasurable anticipation—as if she were expecting a compliment from someone whose opinion of her really mattered. What a ridiculous idea! This man's opinion meant absolutely nothing to her—which, she ruefully admitted, was just as well, since it was abundantly plain that he saw nothing attractive in her at all! His eyes had now travelled up to her hair; it was bright in the morning sunshine, with enchanting glints of colour from dark brown to russet-gold. Short and kinked up at the sides, and teased attractively by the breeze, it added a charmingly youthful effect to her elfin features.

The silence continued, with Kort's attention now on what Sally was wearing—the snow-white shirt, tucked into the tight-fitting belt of her dark blue jeans, the navy sandals revealing her brown toes and polished nails. At her throat she wore a brightly-coloured silk scarf, knotted and with the ends pushed into the open neck of her shirt.

Under such a searching and critical scrutiny it was not surprising that Sally's face suffused with colour. But it was the strange unfathomable pulsating of her heart which affected her more deeply than anything else. She could find no cause for it, nor was there any sense in it, since she was not afraid of this man. Afraid....

Was it the sensation of fear she was experiencing? She had vaguely accepted this as an explanation even while one half of her mind told her it most certainly was not fear. What, then, was this strange, inexplicable sensation—this dim stirring of an emotion both new and faintly disturbing?

Kort broke the silence, passing some casual remark about a proposed visit by Ray to Walleroo Creek.

'I expect,' he added, and even yet again there was a quirk of amusement in his voice, 'that if Ray does decide on this visit, the object of which is to let Nicole take a look at the homestead, you'll accompany them as chaperon to your foster-sister?'

'It's more than likely that she'll ask me to go.'

His eyes flickered.

'I can assure you she'll be safe with Ray,' he said.

'I believe you,' Sally answered him seriously. 'However, I think I'd better see the homestead too, because, as perhaps you know, Nicole's mother must be reassured about the home which Nicole might one day occupy.'

'Might?' he echoed. 'Is there some doubt about the marriage taking place?'

Sally looked squarely at him.

'Tell me, Mr Lander, can you yourself be sure it'll take place?'

He frowned at her then and said, an odd inflection in his voice,

'I surmise that you know something which I don't?'

She hesitated, although she had no intention of revealing any part of the conversation which she had had with his brother.

'You advised your brother to wait,' she said.

'I did, and so did you.'

She nodded her head.

'They've decided to take our advice.'

'So far so good.' Kort paused a moment. 'We do at least agree on one thing,' he added, and a strange compulsion urged her to say,

'We seem to have had a more amicable discussion than usual, Mr Lander.'

His blue eyes held mirth, reflecting the amusement in his tones as he said,

'A pleasant interlude between antagonists, eh?'

She found herself laughing, and just at that moment a jacko laughed too, with the result that Kort's sense of humour came right to the fore and, to Sally's amazement, he joined in. She said, noticing his intention of leaving her,

'Yes, Mr Lander; it was a pleasant interlude between antagonists.' She looked up at him. 'A truce, as it were.'

His laughter had faded now and the more familiar austerity returned to his features.

'A truce? Now I wonder just how long it will last?'

Sally shrugged philosophically.

'Time alone will tell, Mr Lander,' she said, and he merely nodded in agreement. He left her then, and she made her way across the lawn towards the homestead, her brow furrowed in thought. His was a complex character, she decided, having to admit to there being something inordinately attractive about him in that more amicable and gracious mood in which she had found him this morning.

CHAPTER FOUR

ANOTHER fortnight elapsed uneventfully, but Sally's thoughts inevitably kept returning to the conversation which had taken place between Ray and herself, and she knew serious misgivings as the time for Dora's return drew near. Ray came to her one day as she stood by one of the saddling paddocks waiting for one of the rouseabouts to saddle the horse which Kort Lander had for the past week permitted her to ride. Smilingly she turned, and looked up into his eyes.

His own eyes were shaded; she guessed at the reason even before he spoke.

'I've heard from Dora, over the air,' he said, his tone unusually lifeless and quiet. 'She wants to see me—as soon as possible.'

A small silence followed, Sally finding herself unable to comment. Ray spoke again, telling Sally that the message had come through when he was out. His brother had received it and passed it on to Ray.

'Was he—angry at all?' inquired Sally curiously.

Ray frowned uncertainly.

'It was impossible to tell.' Suddenly he grimaced. 'You haven't known him long, but I expect that already you've decided he can hide his feelings without the least difficulty?'

She nodded her head, her eyes straying fleetingly to the rouseabout who now had the horse ready and waiting for her to mount him.

'He's enigmatical, that's for sure,' she replied. 'I

also find him puzzling in another way.'

'You do?'

'That stern, formidable side which he almost always shows to the world is obviously a very real part of his disposition, but I sense another side to his nature.'

Ray's brows shot up a fraction.

'Nicole told me you laughed at the idea of Kort's having a heart.'

Sally coloured.

'I admit to saying he couldn't be hurt,' she murmured after a space. 'He seems both hard and invulnerable where emotions are concerned.' She glanced apologetically at him, vitally aware of the deep respect this boy had for his brother. 'I hope I haven't offended you by my frankness,' she added, and Ray instantly shook his head.

'No, of course you haven't. I like honesty. However, you appear to have contradicted yourself.'

'By saying he was hard and yet there's another side to his nature?'

'Yes, that's right.'

The rouseabout was becoming impatient and, excusing herself for a moment, Sally took the reins and led the horse towards the place where Ray was standing.

'I can't fully explain the light in which I regard your brother, Ray,' she said, frowning in thought. 'I'm sure he's hard, yet when he displays humour he changes so dramatically that his whole personality seems to undergo a transformation.'

Ray looked curiously at her; she was blushing, and her fingers fidgeted with the reins she held in her hand.

'I thought that you and Kort were sworn enemies,'

he said bluntly. 'Yet now you appear to have found something attractive in him—and are actually admitting that you've found it.'

She glanced away, her thoughts confused. She changed the subject ... and knew it was a defensive move, since she had no desire to discuss Kort any further at this time.

'You were saying that Dora wants to see you?'

'She asked that I go over as soon as I can.'

'And you don't know what to say to her?' She glanced up at him. 'So you don't want to go? Is that it?'

'Yes.'

'You'll have to see her. You owe it to her to give the answer you promised.'

He nodded unhappily.

'I expect I do owe it to her. Yet I don't know what to tell her.'

'You'll have to tell her that Nicole is here, of course.' Although fully aware that this could only increase Ray's anxiety, Sally felt he ought to be brought face to face with the inevitable at once. 'You can't hide her away, can you?'

Ray shook his head.

'I've never been so confused in my life!' he exclaimed almost angrily. 'I just don't know what to do!'

Sally frowned, impatient at his weakness. What a vast difference there was in the characters of the two brothers!

'It's because of this confusion that you changed your mind about taking Nicole to Walleroo Creek, isn't it?'

Reluctantly he admitted that this was so.

'Has Nicole said anything about my not taking her?' he added.

'She said it was strange that you hadn't pursued the matter. However, she's obviously determined to practise patience. You're a lucky man, Ray. Nicole could be making a fuss over the way you're treating her.'

'Treating her?' he protested. 'I hope you haven't told her about Dora? What I revealed to you was in confidence.'

'I haven't repeated your confidences. But Nicole knows that Kort has chosen a wife for you; she'll soon learn that Dora is the girl.'

'You insinuated that I'm treating her badly,' said Ray, deliberately ignoring Sally's last sentence.

'Not badly,' returned Sally with a patience she did not feel she could maintain very much longer. 'But you've not been as attentive lately as you were during the first week. Nor did you offer any protest when your brother and I advised you to wait for a while before getting married. Have you not realized that, by your docile attitude, you're revealing a lack of enthusiasm?'

'Yes. Make no mistake, Sally, I'm very conscious of my indecision.'

She gave a deep sigh. This evening she would be writing to Nicole's mother, and she had no idea how she was going to make the contents of the letter sound light and reassuring when, deep within her, she was so anxious about the welfare of the girl she had accompanied here.

'I rather think you ought to have a talk with Kort,' she advised at length. 'Make a full confession; tell him that it was his high-handed attitude that caused you to rebel and in consequence to send for Nicole. Say you're undecided about marrying either girl——'

'I can't confess anything like that,' was his sharp rejoinder. 'His opinion of me is low enough as it is. I wouldn't let him know that I brought Nicole here merely because I wanted to resist his authority.'

Sally's patience was fast running out. She turned, and began stroking the horse's head, her eye travelling past him to the shimmering scrubland over which she was eager to ride.

'I'm afraid I myself can't advise you any differently, Ray. If you're not willing to go to your brother with your problem then you'll have to tackle it yourself, won't you?'

Ray frowned at her.

'I had a feeling you'd help me,' he told her sulkily.

'In what possible way can I help you?' she countered shortly.

He paused for a long moment and then,

'You could persuade Nicole that I'm not the kind of man she should marry.'

Silence. Sally's eyes were glinting with anger when at last she spoke.

'I see. So you do know which girl you want to marry?'

Ray bit his lip; he seemed almost ready to cry, she thought.

'No, Sally,' he answered huskily, 'that's just it. I don't know which girl I want to marry.'

'I don't understand?'

'I'm getting to like Nicole, and if there were no obstacles I'd feel I could come to love her dearly. But on the other hand it would be simpler for me to marry Dora.'

Although Sally liked him, there was no doubt that

at this moment she felt nothing but contempt for him.

'Simpler?' she repeated, looking narrowly at him. 'Because of your brother's attitude, of course?'

'A union with Dora's family would please him no end.'

Sally wished she could have said,

'Then for goodness' sake marry the girl!' but of course she refrained, thinking of Nicole who had asserted she was in love with Ray. Were he to inform her of his intention of marrying another girl she would be heartbroken.

'I'm afraid you're going to have to choose between money and love—not that I believe you're anywhere near falling in love with Nicole,' she added, and now it was impossible for her to keep the contempt from her voice. Ray said nothing and after a moment she asked when he proposed to see Dora.

'I ought to go over tomorrow, but I'd rather wait and see her at the shed dance over at Coonabah Creek.'

'But Nicole will be there too. We're all invited.' Sally had been told by Kort that both she and Nicole would be invited to the shed dance given by a friend of his, John Rossiter, who owned the vast cattle station known as Coonabah Creek.

'I shall be able to speak to Dora privately,' Ray was saying, and Sally looked at him. Her attention had been caught by the big homestead car which had swept along the approach to Kort's house. Ray's attention then became caught and she heard him give a little gasp. 'This is Dora now!' he said, and it was plain that he would have done anything to escape. 'It's her father's car, that is,' he amended suddenly, his voice steadying. 'I don't think she's with him.' He turned to Sally. 'Please excuse me. I have a feeling that Dora's father has come over to talk to Kort——'

'About a possible marriage between you and Dora?'

'Yes. I can't think of any other reason why he should be here, because it's a very long way to drive.' Swiftly excusing himself again Ray swung round and hurried away towards the side entrance to the homestead. Sally was left wondering whether Ray was intending to make himself scarce or whether he had decided to face up to his difficulties and join in the discussion between Dora's father and Kort.

Sally was taking an easy pace, keeping the homestead buildings always in sight. The creek with its fringing gum trees drew her eventually to the shade and she dismounted, tethering the horses to a low branch of one of the eucalypts. In the sunlight she caught a glimpse, in the far distance, of a kangaroo and visualised her with a tiny joey in her pouch—a baby that could be no more than an inch long.

A sound close by brought her head around. Kort Lander was approaching at a leisurely trot. Magnificent he looked, astride a beautiful stallion, and something stirred within Sally's breast. She wondered why she felt no annoyance at her peace being disturbed—for it was now obvious that the proud rider meant to stop and speak to her.

'Hello,' was his greeting, spoken cordially but with his customary coolness and superiority of tone. He might be a king, she thought, hoping she could maintain her composure. 'Taking a rest?' He slid from the stallion's back and moved towards the tree where Sally was standing. She was leaning against it, an attractive figure in spotless white shirt and olive green denims.

The breeze had tossed her hair about; it had also brought a healthy brightness to her cheeks. Mechanically she brushed a hand through her hair, as if she desired to give a more favourable impression. His eyes fixed themselves on her fingers, watching their combing movements in some amusement. The sun shone on his own hair as he took off his slouch hat; she noted the sprinklings of grey at the temples. They looked like threads of silver. Tanned face and hands, firm classical features spelling power and a lifetime of authority. The height of him overwhelmed her and yet she continued to tilt her head, meeting his gaze as he brought it slowly from her hand to her eyes.

'I believe you have a visitor,' she murmured at last, aware that it had taken some considerable time for her to say this. Did she really want him to stay with her? No, of course not ... but if this were so, then why had she been so reluctant to inform him of the arrival of Dora's father? 'A car drove up to the homestead as I was coming away—about twenty minutes ago, that was.'

'A car?' he frowned. 'What colour was it?'

'Grey, and large. Ray said it belonged to—to ...' She tailed off, wishing she had stopped after voicing the first three words.

'Yes? To whom?' Kort's tone held curiosity, yet she knew he had no doubts about whose car had arrived at the homestead. 'Well?' he added when she did not speak.

'I suppose it's no secret,' she said, then coloured as she realized how ambiguous this was. 'The car belongs to the father of a girl called Dora,' she added coolly.

Kort Lander's eyes narrowed slightly.

'Ray's told you about Dora?'

69

'He has, yes.'

'Nicole ... does she know about her?'

'Only vaguely, she doesn't regard the girl as really important.'

A small silence fell, broken presently by the whinnying of one of the horses.

'I suppose my brother explained that I very much favour his marrying Dora?' So calm the voice—and arrogant. The arrogance was in the form of a challenge, which Sally accepted with a promptitude born of anger.

'Whether you're offended or not, Mr Lander,' she said, looking squarely at him, 'I'm telling you that you have no right at all to dictate your brother's life for him. His decisions, whether they concern marriage or any other matter of importance, should be made by him alone.'

A glint entered her companion's blue eyes.

'It would appear,' he returned icily, 'that you care little whether or not you offend me!'

'I'm not intending to be blatantly rude, but I'm an honest person and when the necessity arises I speak my mind.'

'Which, I've found, is often!'

'Merely because you and I don't see eye to eye.'

'We did on one particular occasion, remember?'

She nodded her head, frowning inwardly. For some quite incomprehensible reason she was wishing that she and the boss of Grey River Downs could more often find themselves in agreement.

'To get back to this girl—Dora,' she murmured at last. 'Apart from the material advantage of a marriage between her and Ray, is there some other reason for your wanting him to marry her?'

70

'She has the experience required for the position she would hold as wife of one of the wealthiest landowners in the country. She is also an Australian——'

'What have you against Englishwomen?' she flashed. 'With travel being what it is today your idea's antiquated!'

To her surprise he appeared to be faintly amused by her outburst.

'You're very protective of your young charge, Miss Prentice. It's plain that you intend to fight to the limit to get her married to my brother.'

She turned, putting out a hand to pat her horse's gleaming neck.

'You seem to have forgotten already something of which you have only a few minutes ago reminded me. I agreed with you that Nicole should wait.'

'But you never intended she should abandon the idea of marriage with my brother.'

She swung about again, to search his eyes.

'You yourself hoped that a delay would be the prelude to the end of the affair?'

Kort inclined his head.

'I still hope the affair will end,' he told her quietly.

'You don't care that Ray might ruin his whole life by marriage with a girl he doesn't love?'

A sneer replaced the amused curve of his lips.

'Love!' he scoffed, derision in his gaze. 'Why trouble about anything so fleeting as love?'

Her eyes challenged as she returned,

'You yourself attach far more importance to the practicalities of life?'

'Not *more* importance—*every* importance.'

'You attach no importance whatsoever to love?' She was thinking of his romance, and wondering if he himself was recalling it. That it was the cause of his cynicism she did not doubt, and she found herself vaguely deciding that it was a pity he had allowed it to influence his life the way it had.

'Love is merely the idle fancy of the female sex.'

She stared, colouring faintly because he was displaying amusement and contempt and pity all at one and the same time.

'What a poor opinion you have of my sex, Mr Lander!'

'I'm sorry if it touches your ego,' he returned with a hint of laughter in his voice. 'But, like you, I'm an honest person and when the necessity arises I speak my mind.'

Her colour deepened at his satirical use of her own words.

'Hadn't you better see to your visitor?' she said, unable to find anything scathing enough with which to answer his galling sarcasm concerning her sex.

He laughed outright.

'Once again I seem to have floored you, Miss Prentice. It must be rather frustrating for a woman to find she's lost for words.'

Suddenly her temper blazed; she forgot completely her earlier resolution never to allow him to witness her anger.

'What an ill-mannered, pompous man you are! I wish with all my heart this business of Nicole and Ray were settled, one way or the other! Because then I'd be free to leave the—the hospitality which you've so reluctantly offered me!' She was seething, and with every word uttered she became even more furious. 'No, you needn't retaliate by declaring me to be the rudest woman you've ever met! If I am ill-mannered it's only because you've persistently goaded me! And now,' she added with a swift attempt at dignity, 'please leave me! I was peacefully enjoying the countryside until you came along and inflicted your unwanted presence upon me!'

An awful silence followed, with Kort, just as angry as she, colouring faintly as a thread of crimson crept up each side of his jaw. His eyes blazed as they looked piercingly into hers. She knew without any doubt at all that he would like to have slapped her—knew this even before he spoke.

'What you're in need of,' he said in vibrating tones, 'is a damned good box on the ears!' And on that parting shot he swung effortlessly into the saddle and rode off in a cloud of dust.

Sally stared after him, watching his figure until it became lost to view. In her heart something strange was affording her some uneasiness. She hated to admit it, but Kort's unfriendliness had begun to hurt in a way she failed to understand. It was not as if she cared a jot about his opinion, either of her personally or of women in general. Nor did she believe she could be totally comfortable in his presence no matter how he might treat her. Even a sociable Mr Kort Lander would be formidable, she thought. So why should she be experiencing this rather dejected feeling, this vague regret at the antagonism which not only existed between them, but which was increasing with every encounter they had with one another?

With a sigh she mounted her horse and slowly rode in the direction which Kort had taken. The sun was no longer warm, not bright, even. The landscape no longer pleased her; the pretty pink galahs annoyed her by their screaming; the distant mountains, old as the earth itself, looked gaunt and grey and formidable. The vast spinifex plains looked drab; the peace and solitude she had so recently enjoyed became oppressive.

She wanted nothing so much as to be able to go home.

Ray was by the paddock when she arrived there to hand over the horse to the rouseabout. Glancing at him curiously, she asked,

'Did you talk to Dora's father?'

'Yes. I was with him until a short while ago. Kort wasn't about, so I was forced to show good manners and entertain him.'

'You talked about his daughter?' The rouseabout was taking the reins from her hand; she smiled and thanked him, then turned to Ray again.

'No. Strangely enough he didn't mention her at all. He'd come over on different business altogether. It's something about the movement of the cattle. We move it by air,' he added by way of explanation. But that was as far as he did go, so Sally was left in the dark as to why Dora's father had come. She shrugged, not in the least interested, anyway.

'So your original intention of seeing Dora at the shed dance still stands?'

Ray nodded his head.

'Yes. I suppose you consider me a shirker. But I'm not, really. It's just that I want time to sort myself out.'

Sally made no comment; in her opinion Ray would need considerable time in which to sort himself out, certainly more than the eight days which would elapse before the evening of the shed dance at Coonibah Creek.

That evening Ray seemed morose and when dinner

was over Nicole sought Sally out and asked if she too had noticed this.

'I must admit I did,' replied Sally, unable to lie to Nicole.

'He seems to have something on his mind.'

'I expect it's his brother.' Sally's tone was sharp and Nicole said, changing the subject,

'Are you and Kort still at loggerheads?'

'I suppose that is how you could put it.' Unnecessarily Sally smoothed the front of her dress. It was strange how the mention of Kort Lander had brought about a mixture of anger and regret. The anger she could explain, but the regret ...?

Watching her, Nicole remained silent, admiring the lovely picture she made. The dress was of black velvet, trimmed with sequins and gold braid. It was long and fitting and low at the neck, revealing shapely shoulders and the alluring curve of her breasts.

'I wish you and Kort weren't enemies——' Nicole broke off abruptly, puzzled as to the reason for her words.

'It's really the oddest thing that we are,' returned Sally with a frown. 'I can't think why we should always rub one another up the wrong way, but we do. He's so arrogant and superior. I never feel comfortable, so I expect I adopt a defensive attitude which makes me say horrid things to him.'

Nicole's eyes opened very wide indeed.

'You say horrid things to him?' she gasped. 'I don't know how you could dare!'

'He aggravates me so.'

'And you obviously aggravate him.'

'Undoubtedly I do.'

'Here he is now. I wonder where Ray is? He said

75

we'd go for a stroll after dinner.'

Both girls were standing by the open window of the sitting-room and Kort was coming along the verandah which ran the full length of the front of the house. Stopping as he reached them, he politely spread a hand, indicating the table, and said, in his slow yet rich Australian drawl,

'Aren't you two girls having coffee?'

'Yes,' timidly from Nicole, but she did add, 'Ray was supposed to be taking me for a stroll, but I don't know where he disappeared to.'

Kort looked at her, examining her face by the light of the standard lamp in the sitting-room behind her.

'You don't appear to be too happy,' he commented, surprising them both. 'Have you quarrelled with Ray?'

Sally shot him a glance. Was he hoping that the couple would have differences, and so simplify the carrying out of his own pet scheme? Catching the glance, and instantly grasping the meaning of it, Kort lifted his brows in a gesture of arrogance.

'Did you wish to make some comment, Miss Prentice?'

A sharp intake of her breath was his only answer for a long unpleasant moment.

'You obviously read my glance,' replied Sally at last, and without any attempt at diplomacy. 'No, Mr Lander, I have no comment to make—simply because you don't require me to explain what I am thinking.'

'Point taken, Miss Prentice. You're a clever woman, I must grant you that.' He turned to Nicole again. 'You're puzzled, child. Let me explain. Your foster-sister suspects me of harbouring hopes of you and Ray quarrelling, so that you'll part company——'

'Oh, how can you say so!' protested Nicole angrily. 'Sally would never be so uncharitable as to have suspicions of that nature! You don't know her very well, Kort, for if you did you'd know that she's sweet-natured and kind and never has she been quarrelsome in the whole of her life——'

'Nicole dear,' interrupted Sally, blushing hotly under the amused—and interested—stare of her host. 'Mr Lander doesn't want to hear such nonsense.'

'It isn't nonsense!'

'And I do want to hear it,' softly from Kort, whose eyes had never left Sally's flushed face. 'Tell me more about this paragon of all the virtues,' he invited presently, transferring his attention momentarily from Sally to Nicole.

'Please——' began Sally, but a wave of an imperious hand brought her to a stop.

'Nicole—tell me some more.' But at this moment Ray appeared, and broke in to apologize for his short absence. Sally heard him say that he had had to attend to a troublesome cut on his finger, then invited Nicole to take the stroll with him. Forgetting all about the coffee to which Kort had invited her, Nicole eagerly took Ray's arm and together they went along the verandah, descended the wooden steps at the end, and disappeared into the darkness of the garden.

A long moment elapsed before Kort spoke to Sally.

'So we take our coffee on our own, Miss Prentice.'

She nodded, unconsciously biting her lip. She suddenly realized that it could all be so pleasant, out here on the verandah, with the cool evening breeze dispelling the heat of the day, and the tranquil silence of the landscape around them. Yes, it could all have been so pleasant—had not such enmity grown up between

Kort and herself.

He seemed to be waiting for her to speak and she murmured softly,

'Yes, Mr Lander, we take coffee on our own.'

'I could invite Ruff and Tyler—if you would prefer not to be alone with me?'

Sally gave him a speaking glance and retorted,

'Must you always be so infuriatingly provoking?'

All he did was to laugh, and then he pulled out a chair for her, waiting until she became seated before moving round to take possession of the chair opposite to her. Lifting a hand, he pulled a bell-rope.

'What do you say to our having another interlude of harmony?' he invited unexpectedly. 'After all, we can't just sit here, drinking coffee together and have a slanging match, can we?'

He was laughing with his eyes and she suddenly caught her breath. The whole atmosphere was filled with romance and she herself knew a deep and pleasant sensation of well-being and happiness. She smiled, and her eyes held a sparkle as she answered, readily and in the friendliest tones she had ever used to him,

'No, of course we can't. I'm all for the interlude of harmony you mention.'

A responding smile appeared, to soften his face again, just as the laughter had softened it. He opened his mouth to speak, but closed it again as Susannah appeared with the coffee tray. Sally realized she had been expectant, wanting to hear him speak. Now, she felt instinctively that she had lost something, that whatever he had meant to say would now remain unsaid. What was it he had drawn back on the appearance of his servant? Something pleasant, Sally knew, and a faint sigh escaped her. But Kort failed to hear it, and when the lubra had gone he asked Sally to pour the coffee. As she did so she was all the time aware of his eyes upon her; she gave him his coffee, glad of the dimmed light because she was sure her colour had risen under his most searching scrutiny.

'Tell me about yourself,' was his surprising invitation, and he leant back comfortably in his chair, preparing to spend the next few minutes in listening to her quiet, musical voice as she told him about her parents' deaths and her going to live with Nicole's mother.

CHAPTER FIVE

SALLY did not know whether or not it was her imagination, but it did seem that Kort's attitude towards her had changed a little since the evening when on his invitation, she had told him more about herself. He had put a few questions, and in the end he had a fairly comprehensive picture of what her life had been like since she was left an orphan at so early an age. And as if to strengthen the idea of this change in his attitude, he offered to fly both her and Nicole to the nearest town, Morrawilla, so that they could buy dresses for the shed dance. The offer was made when Nicole declared she had 'nothing to wear' for the occasion. Sally had merely laughed, fully aware that Mrs Rotherham had spared no expense in fitting out her daughter's wardrobe for the trip. Ray was indisposed, the cut on his hand having turned septic so that he was feeling too ill to fly the plane. Hence the unexpected offer made by the boss. Nicole readily accepted; Sally was more reserved, but accepted for all that.

'Not that I want to buy a dress,' she added. 'I shall have to make do with my white dress.'

Kort said, his eyes sweeping her lovely slender figure,

'If it's the one which is ruched in the middle then it'll do very well.'

Sally looked amazed. She had not for one moment realized he could have had so much interest in her to notice anything she wore. The white dress in question had been worn once, for dinner. Long and full-skirted, it was of a most unusual style, the material appearing to have been picked up by the designer, and ruched tightly into a place between the waist and neckline. Over the ruching was placed a circle of the material, this being stiffened, and edged with a cord covered with the satin. The sleeves were very full, and came from the waistline, then gathered into a tight cuff. Sally had paid a large amount of money for the dress and the shopkeeper had told her that the style originated in South America. Most certainly it was distinctive, and Sally felt that it suited her to perfection.

And Kort had noticed it....

The thought brought a surge of pleasure to her, for it was certainly flattering for a man as indifferent towards women as Kort Lander to have taken notice of what she had worn.

He had also said it would do very well. This comment began to puzzle her a little. It was almost as if *he* were the one to say whether or not he wanted her to wear that particular dress!

'You're preoccupied, Miss Prentice.' Kort's voice brought a sudden smile to Sally's lips. She was sitting by him in the aeroplane, and they were flying over the wilderness of mallee scrub.

'I was thinking of my dress,' she returned with absolute frankness.

'The white one?' from Nicole before he could speak. 'It's lovely! Will you pass it on to me when you're tired of it?' she added teasingly.

'Perhaps. But I don't think I shall get tired of it for a very long time.'

'You'll wear it till it wilts?' Amusement edged Kort Lander's tones. 'Like the "Alice Blue Gown"?' Sally laughed but made no answer. 'Why were you thinking about it?' added Kort curiously, turning his head to look at her profile.

She wondered if she had coloured at his question. She managed to say lightly,

'Oh, no particular reason——'

'Liar,' he interrupted, softly and slowly. 'I know why you were thinking about it, so don't trouble to tell me a fib.'

Nicole looked swiftly from one to the other, astonishment in her eyes. Sally glanced away, embarrassed by the situation, a situation which seemed to have been created deliberately, by Kort Lander.

'Why was she thinking about it, Kort?' asked Nicole when the silence continued.

'If Sally won't tell you herself then I'm sure I won't,' was Kort's reply.

'Sally....' from Nicole strangely. 'I think it's time you two did become more friendly——'

'Nicole!' broke in Sally, hot now as her embarrassment increased. 'Please don't——'

'I must say I'm in complete agreement with Nicole,' intervened Kort coolly, turning his head again to glance at Sally's profile. 'I can't imagine our being so formal as to be saying "Miss Prentice and Mr Lander" at the shed dance tomorrow night. These occasions, though lavishly laid on by whoever organizes them, are, for all that, rather homely, intimate affairs. No one ever stands on ceremony. So you see, Sally, you'll have to bring yourself to call me Kort——'

'I couldn't!'

'Nonsense,' interposed Nicole firmly. 'I've thought

for some time that you both ought to bury the hatchet!'

Kort merely laughed, but Sally threw her foster-sister a darkling glance. Nicole grinned triumphantly and said,

'Are you willing to bury the hatchet, Kort?'

'It might interest you to know that Sally and I do actually have "cease fire" interludes now and then.'

'Oh ... I didn't know.'

'Shall we change the subject?' murmured Sally, glancing down. 'Nicole, look at those kangaroos—over there.'

Kort looked down, and commented, and from then on the conversation was centred on the view below. The town appeared, a few shops, a bank and a café at the end of a railroad. Yet the store provided for most needs and Nicole managed to buy herself an evening skirt and pale blue frilly blouse. Kort had gone off to the bank, but met them for lunch, which they had out in the open air. Altogether it was one of the most enjoyable days Sally had ever spent; most certainly it was the pleasantest day she had spent since coming to Grey River Downs.

'Have you made an appointment for your hair to be washed and set?' Nicole was asking at breakfast the following morning. 'My appointment's for ten o'clock.'

'Mine's for eleven.' The hairdressing saloon was just one of the modern amenities to be found on any cattle station of the magnitude of Grey River Downs. There was a school, shops, hospital and a library—these to serve the people living in the lovely modern bungalows that formed a small estate about half a mile from the homestead itself. The stockriders' wives and families occupied these bungalows; there was also a small block of flats for those stockmen who were single and preferred to have their own private accommodation. Tyler and Ruff chose to live at the homestead, and Ray had said that on one occasion more than a dozen men had lived in. However, since the flats had been built Kort preferred that the men should occupy their own private apartments. Some of course were on the move all the time, those wanderers who were content to live on canned meat and damper and billy tea.

'I'm so excited!' exclaimed Nicole as she entered Sally's bedroom later in the day. 'A shed dance! It'll be so new and unusual!'

'Unusual for us, but not for anyone else.' Sally smiled affectionately at her foster-sister, admiring the skirt and blouse she had bought yesterday in town. 'I must hurry; we've to be away by half-past four.'

'Imagine having a hundred-mile drive before we get there!'

'Kort's having to drive, isn't he?'

Nicole nodded her head.

'Ray's hand is still giving him some pain.'

'I'm sorry about that.' Sally was wondering how he was feeling about the forthcoming encounter with Dora. She surmised that he was not very happy at all. Early yesterday morning, just before she was departing for Morrawilla, she had talked to Ray, but he was still confused in mind and said outright that he wished he could go away somewhere, so that he could think things out.

'I don't really mind.' Nicole had moved over to the dressing table and her eyes met Sally's. Sally was vigorously brushing her hair, not at all liking the formal way the hairdresser had set it. 'Ray and I can sit in the back and holds hands.'

Sally frowned into the mirror.

'I don't particularly want to sit in the front with Kort, Nicole. Do you mind very much if I take the back seat?'

'I do,' was Nicole's firm rejoinder. 'I think it's stupid of you two to carry on as you are doing. Also, I have to say that in my opinion Kort's ready to be real friendly—but you, Sally, seem determined not to be nice to him.'

'You don't understand, Nicole. When we're alone Kort is horrid to me. He's arrogant and superior and patronizing and insufferable! He's bossy and over-bearing and——'

'Oh, give up!' laughed Nicole. 'I refuse to believe that any man could be as abominable as that!'

Sally herself had to laugh.

'Perhaps I was rather free with the adjectives,' she owned, thinking of that evening when Kort had wanted to know about her life in England. That had been a most pleasant interlude, and Kort had even managed to unbend sufficiently to say, as he bade her good night,

'I've enjoyed our little talk, Miss Prentice. We must have another some time.'

'The car's here—outside the homestead.' Nicole had moved over to the window on hearing a sound, and she now saw that Kort was standing beside the big overlanding car. Ray appeared and got into the back. Kort glanced upwards and Nicole waved a hand. 'You know,' she murmured, turning to watch as Sally used the perfume spray on her hair and her wrists, 'at first I had the impression that Kort looked down on me. But now ... well, he's not so bad after all.'

Sally swung round on the stool. Nicole's eyes were dreamy. . . .

'I hope you're not going to complicate matters by having a crush on the boss of Grey River Downs!' she cried before she could stop herself. 'Things are bad enough as they are!'

'What on earth do you mean?'

'Oh, nothing! Come on. Kort won't contain his patience much longer!'

'You sound in a bad temper, Sally. And another thing—don't talk such nonsense about my having a crush on Kort. I love Ray.'

Rising and taking up her cloak and evening bag, Sally looked at her foster-sister.

'You're sure?'

'Of course I'm sure,' frowned Nicole. 'What's the matter with you, Sally? You know very well that I'm in love with Ray.'

'And he?'

'He needs a little more time to get to know me—but he loves me. I'm fairly sure of that.'

Sally gave a sigh and swept from the room, closely followed by Nicole. What a muddle!

But little did she know that the muddle would be greater than ever before the night was out!

They arrived at a few minutes to eight, driving on to a forecourt and parking among a medley of station wagons, utilities, land-rovers and overlanding cars. The homestead was well illuminated, but it was the shed which caught the attention of the two girls. Numerous coloured lights festooned the entire building; fountains were illuminated to one side of it. The surrounding trees were also highlighted with coloured lanterns and in all it was a most romantic setting. Music drifted softly through the open windows on to the verandah where John Rossiter and his wife, Trudy, stood waiting to receive their guests. Sally and Nicole were introduced as friends of Ray, and were instantly accepted with the utmost cordiality. Drinks were offered and then the four drifted into the huge wooden barn. Ray instantly took Nicole into his arms; Sally stood looking around, at those young ladies who were not dancing, and tried to pick out the girl, Dora. But it was another girl to whom her eyes kept on returning, a girl who could not be Dora, because Ray had described Dora as a brunette, and this devastatingly beautiful girl was a glorious golden blonde.

'Shall we dance?' Kort spoke at the same instant that the girl saw him. Sally noticed her eyes move to herself, and then Kort was speaking, and at the same time taking Sally by the arm and leading her on to the dance floor.

She glanced up, into his face ... and frowned in puzzlement at the expression of severity she noticed there. His mouth was tight, his eyes hard—like metal. The fine lines of his jaw were flexed, and in his throat a muscle twitched strangely. He seemed caught in the grip of some strong emotion, yet his voice betrayed nothing of this when at length he spoke.

'Relax, Sally. You're as stiff as a poker!'

'How unflattering!' she retorted. 'I've never been told I'm stiff.'

Kort laughed, and all the severity was dispelled.

'Perhaps I was a little strong in my description. You were tensed. Was something wrong?'

She shook her head, unable to explain that the closeness of him did something to her, creating a sort of electric current within her so that every nerve seemed to be vibrating.

'No, nothing.'

'Well, you're more relaxed now.' He glanced down, into her flushed face, and his eyes smiled. She caught her breath, bewildered even while she owned that the touch of his hand was the most pleasant experience she had ever known. His arm about her too was comforting, protective. . . .

She gave herself a mental shake and paid attention to her steps. She and Kort had moved round the outside of the floor and they were suddenly close to the lovely blonde who had fixed Sally's attention a few minutes earlier. The girl looked into Kort's face and smiled. He nodded briefly and passed on.

Later, the girl was being introduced to Sally. She had approached Kort immediately he and Sally came off the floor and took possession of two chairs on the verandah.

'Kort! How wonderful to see you again!' The voice, low and sensuously husky, purred close to Kort's ear. He stood up, his face impassive, and said quietly,

'Sally, meet Gracia.'

'How do you do?' Both girls spoke together; both stared into each other's face. Kort then murmured their surnames, stressing the Mrs when he said,

'Mrs Lester.'

The girl coloured a little but retained her composure. Sally knew without being told that this girl was Kort's old flame, the one who had jilted him to marry a man living in Sydney. And now she was a widow. . . .

'Tell me about things,' invited Gracia, glancing

round for a chair. Kort gave her his and fetched another. Sally tried to read his thoughts as he returned to the table. His face was an inscrutable mask.

'What things?' he asked when he was seated.

'The station, and what's been happening all over the place.'

'I expect your father's kept you well informed,' he said without much expression.

Put out a little, the girl fell silent. But after a while she asked if Sally was a visitor to Coonabah Creek.

'She's a visitor at Grey River Downs.'

'Oh. . . .' Gracia seemed taken aback. 'I took it for granted that she was staying here.'

'Why?'

Gracia shrugged her elegant shoulders.

'I suppose it was silly of me to form a conclusion like that. It isn't often you have females staying with you.'

'I have two at present, one of whom is a friend of Ray.'

'I see. . . .' The girl's eyes settled disconcertingly on Sally's face. 'And Sally . . .?'

How ill-mannered, thought Sally, feeling ready to get up and leave Kort with his ex-girl-friend.

'Sally happens to be a friend of *mine*.' So cool the tone! Sally almost gave a start, then realized she would be giving the girl something to think about and just in time she collected herself. So he was intending to make the girl jealous, was he? Sally saw at once the reason for the change in him of recent days. He knew he would be meeting Gracia at the shed dance and he meant to convince her that he had found someone else. Perhaps he would relent—after he had made use of Sally for a time—and return his attention to the girl he had once loved. Meanwhile he would teach her a lesson ... at Sally's expense.

'A friend of yours? How nice. Er—have you been friends for long?'

'Gracia,' said Kort in level tones, 'you're asking pertinent questions which neither Sally nor I are intending to answer. In any case, I must ask you to excuse us, as I have to introduce Sally to some friends of mine who have just arrived.' Rising with a sort of regal grace, Kort extended a hand to Sally, who instantly put hers into it. She rose, murmured a polite 'Excuse me' and left the table. Her feelings were mixed. On the one hand she was angrily indignant at being used, especially by a man who up till now had treated her with such lack of gallantry. Yet on the other hand she knew a strange inexplicable reluctance to let Kort down. It was all most illogical and, impatient both with herself and with Kort, she dismissed the matter temporarily from her mind as, having been introduced to the couple who had just arrived, Eunice and Jeffrey Stein, she found herself taking part in a pleasant conversation. Then off she was swung once again, into the dance, with Kort now flattering her by telling her she danced delightfully. Was he hoping to make her blush ... so that Gracia would notice? Perhaps he was endeavouring to bring out a spontaneous smile, or a little exclamation. Well, he could try again ... and again....

'Is something wrong?' he was asking later in the evening when, having taken her to the refreshment tent, he looked down into her expressionless face.

'No. What could be wrong?'

'You're very quiet.'

'That's not any change for me. I like being quiet.'

'Have I monopolized you? I did think Ray might come to you for a dance, but he appears to be fully occupied by two girls only—Nicole and Dora.'

Diverted, Sally forgot her intention of retaining a coolness towards him.

'Yes, I've noticed. You know, Kort, I suppose that he's confused?' This was as far as Sally meant to go—but at the same time she desired to open some sort of discussion regarding Ray. There would be no telling tales out of school on her part, but on the other hand she owed a loyalty to her foster-mother and she now decided she must know something definite about the position between Ray and Nicole. 'Do you still hope for the affair between Nicole and Ray to come to an end?'

'Nicole, I've decided, is a charming young lady. But I still consider her unsuitable to hold the position of wife to Ray.'

'Ray tells me that his estate is small. If this is so then surely Nicole can cope——'

'Ray's estate is small—by comparison to Grey River Downs, that is. However, he will inherit a much vaster estate one day——'

'One day? In forty or fifty years' time?'

Kort's lips twitched.

'You think I shall live to be eighty?'

'Yes, I should think so.'

'How confident that sounds!'

'Here, in the open air, and with the pace of life so much slower than in a town, I should imagine people live much longer.'

For a second he seemed ready with an answer on his lips, but he changed his mind and instead asked her what she wanted to eat. Handing her a plate, he stood beside her, a spoon and fork poised in his hand, ready to serve her from any dish she might choose.

When she had all she wanted he found a table in the open and they sat down. Several friends of Kort's stopped to have a word with him and then passed on. Sally had previously been introduced to them all and she found herself confused by the medley of names. However, it did not trouble her overmuch that she failed to remember; it was not as if she would ever meet them again after tonight.

'Is the breeze too strong for you?' he asked concernedly, seeing her put up a hand to her hair. Sally shook her head.

'I like it,' she told him with a smile.

'It doesn't matter that you don't always appear immaculate, then?'

'No, of course not.' So Gracia was fastidious over her appearance, was she? Kort was comparing, and Sally wondered which one of them—Gracia or herself—won the top mark.

'You were wanting to talk about Ray and Nicole?' Kort spoke after noticing Dora go past with the son of a ranch manager.

'I told you a lot about my foster-mother,' she responded, following the direction of his gaze. 'I think you understand just how wonderful she was to me?'

'I think I do,' he agreed.

'And so you'll also understand that I owe her a lot in return?' Kort merely inclined his head and Sally continued, 'I write to her regularly, but I'm not fully honest in my letters. Kort, I'm troubled about the effect on my foster-mother should Nicole return to her with a broken heart.'

Kort's lips twitched in that particularly attractive

way which Sally had witnessed several times this evening. But what he said did not in any way please her.

'You already know my opinions about love.'

'A woman's imagination? It has no depth?'

'Nicole is too young to know what love is,' he returned, and because he had dodged the issue Sally could not resist the riposte,

'Many people have fallen in love at a very young age.'

His eyes glinted and she instantly regretted her words. However, he did not mention his own love affair; she had not expected him to do so.

'Ray would be far better off with Dora,' he said at length.

'Do you really believe you have the right to plan the course of your brother's life?'

'My superiority of age gives me the right to advise.'

'And if he doesn't choose to take that advice?'

'Be it on his own head. He'll live to regret it.'

'You're so pompous and self-opinionated!'

'Sally,' he murmured, indicating the untouched food on her plate, 'you're becoming heated again. I shan't quarrel with you tonight, so you might as well cease your endeavours and concentrate on this delicious food.'

She glared at him, but then laughed.

'I don't want to quarrel with you,' she said, surprising herself more than him.

'I'm glad to hear it. Eat up and we'll take a stroll out there in the moonlight.'

She glanced swiftly at him.

'In the moonlight? I can't see any moon.'

'It's behind the clouds.' Kort put his fork into a sausage and lifted it to his mouth.

'I can't see any clouds, either.'

What he would have said to that Sally did not know, as, looking up, she found herself staring into the eyes of the girl with whom Kort had once been in love.

'Do you mind if I join you?' Gracia carried a plate on which was a solitary sandwich and a tomato. 'I can't find a vacant place to sit.'

'Do sit here,' returned Kort with cold politeness. 'We're just going, anyway, so you'll have the table all to yourself.' He glanced at Sally's plate. She hesitated and then, drawn by some inexplicable compulsion, she left the food on her plate and, rising, took the hand he was extending towards her.

'That,' she said rather severely when they were some distance from the table, 'was not very good manners at all.'

'You find fault with my manners?'

'I always have done.'

Kort gave an amused laugh. He turned his head to look at her, but his eyes were caught by her hair. It was dancing in the breeze.

'Come,' he said, 'and let's take that stroll. Moonlight or not, it should be most enjoyable!'

CHAPTER SIX

THE night was starry, the heavens deep purple. Lights shone out from the barn and the trees surrounding it. Sally moved away from the closeness of her companion, but was still vitally aware of his magnetism. Tinglings of pleasure shot through her as, taking a stride to close the distance she had put between them, Kort took hold of her hand. She glanced back. Gracia was standing now, and her head was turned in their direction. Sally's first instinct was to snatch her hand away, but something held her back. Yet why should she help Kort in his schemes? If he wanted a pawn then let him look elsewhere!

'We didn't manage to get very far in our discussion on Ray and Nicole,' he commented after a while. They had left the barn well behind and now he released her hand. She said levelly,

'Let's leave that for the moment. Tell me, why this sudden change in your attitude towards me?' She played at innocence, deciding that all was fair in his particular kind of war.

'Change?'

'Holding my hand. Judging by the way you've been with me up till now I should have thought that I was the last woman you'd want to be so intimate with.'

'You call holding hands intimate?' he asked in some amusement. 'What a strange girl! I was merely making sure you didn't miss your footing on those rough stones back there.'

'You——!' She bit back the rest, remembering that she had decided to indulge in her own little game. Why have a quarrel when she did not want one? And why not allow him to continue taking her for an idiot?—for that was surely what he was taking her for, changing like this when at first he had made it more than plain that he felt nothing but contempt for her in coming over with Nicole—as her nursemaid, he had said.

'I—what?'

'Nothing.' A pause and then, 'About Ray and Nicole.'

'Yes—Ray and Nicole. It's obvious to me that neither of them is in love.'

'Nicole has said she loves your brother.'

'And I've said she's too young to know anything about love.'

'But according to what you said before there isn't any such thing as love.'

'No—only passion.'

She coloured in the darkness.

'There's such a thing as spiritual love.'

'In the minds of idealists only.'

'Are idealists only female?' she was quick to ask, and Kort gave a short laugh.

'So you're endeavouring to trap me, eh?'

'You haven't answered my question.'

He stopped, and stared down in the dimness, into her upturned face.

'Tell me, Sally, what will you have gained if I admit that there are idealists among men as well as women?'

'Satisfaction,' she replied briefly, and before she could guess at his intention he was giving her a good shake. And then, somehow, she found herself closing irresistibly towards his hard and sinewed body as a strange current raced through her whole being. Kort seemed to pause, but fleetingly, and then she was in his arms; his mouth found hers, forced her lips apart as his own lips took their fill of her fresh young sweetness.

'Oh...!' was all she could say when at last he pulled away from her. He did not release her, but held her arms in a strong and almost hurtful grip. It was a grip of possession, of sheer mastery and dominance. Sally did not resent it; on the contrary, she thrilled to it, unconsciously leaning close again and offering her lips for him to take. A smile touched the fine outline of his mouth before he bent it to hers. Fiercely he kissed her, taking his time over it until she was gasping for breath. Only then did he let her go. She swayed a moment, and automatically put out a hand to grasp the edge of his jacket. His hand came over hers, and then he turned it, gazing at the palm before bringing it to his lips.

No words were said as they began to walk on again. Sally glanced back. There was no one behind them, which meant that Kort had not kissed her for effect— the effect it could have had on his old love.

Why, then, had he kissed her? Could it be that he liked her? Her dress had caused a gasp to leap to many lips this evening, and she had known all along that Kort was proud to be her escort.

'Nicole and Ray,' she murmured presently, because the silence seemed all wrong. It was like the descent of darkness after sunshine. 'We were talking about them.'

'We seem to keep on interrupting ourselves, don't we?'

She nodded.

'I was saying that she's in love with him.'

'Supposing I cede that point,' he said unexpectedly. 'You're still faced with the fact that Ray is not in love with her.'

'I said he's confused. If you would withdraw your authority over this other girl then he'd have a chance to make up his own mind.'

'He ought to have the strength to make up his mind as it is.'

'Perhaps. But he hasn't.'

Again Kort stopped in his tracks, and looked down at her.

'Just how much has he told you—— No, don't deny it! It's plain that he's confided in you. I came upon you having a private talk, remember?'

Sally bit her lip. That incident had completely slipped her memory.

'Yes, I remember. However, I can't repeat what was said to me in confidence.'

'Then I'll make some intelligent guesses——'

'No, I'd rather you didn't.' She would have walked on, but his hand shot out and she found herself firmly held.

'He admitted that he couldn't choose ... because he did not know which one he really wanted. He told you he had made a promise to Dora that he would give her his decision on her return. For your information, he has always liked Dora, and his bringing Nicole over here was merely an impulsive and impractical act of revolt against the advice I'd given him!'

'It was understandable! There had been some kind of arrangement made previously, between Ray's father and Dora's. Why, the whole idea's feudal! What right have parents to dictate to their children like that?'

Kort released her, but neither he nor she moved.

'I agree with you entirely about the parents having no right to dictate. On the other hand, you seem to have forgotten that I've just told you that Ray has always liked Dora. For a time before she went away they met every week. Ray would go over and spend the week-end at her father's house.'

'Yet he was writing to Nicole.'

'A pen-friendship. It meant nothing.'

'He promised marriage, nevertheless.'

'Out of pique. Ray has always had an obstinate streak in him. He's also impulsive, hence his sending for Nicole, as I've said.'

'She came here believing he really wanted to marry her.'

'And he would have married her, had both you and I not advised against a hasty wedding.'

'He did listen to advice on that occasion,' Sally pointed out.

'Yes; only because he himself had had second thoughts about marriage to Nicole.'

Sally had to agree. Kort began walking on again and she fell into step beside him.

'What's to be done, Kort? Do you think I ought to have a talk to Nicole?'

'As you're her guardian it might be advantageous.'

'I'm not really her guardian,' she returned. 'Her mother asked me to come solely because she couldn't come herself, and she naturally disliked the idea of Nicole's coming on her own.'

'I think we should wait a while,' he said thoughtfully. 'Certainly you could talk to Nicole, and endeavour to find out just how deeply her own feelings have become involved. But don't probe any further than that—and certainly don't mention that Ray can't make up his mind.'

'No, I wouldn't dream of it! Nicole doesn't know about his affair with Dora.'

Kort's eyes flickered in the darkness.

'She's bound to suspect something after tonight. Ray's danced as much with Dora as he has with Nicole.'

'Perhaps her eyes will be opened.'

Kort said nothing and for a while they strolled along in silence. It was a harmonious, companionable silence, and Sally thought it very strange that she should not be feeling embarrassed as she reflected on the little scene which had been enacted between her and Kort a few minutes ago. For him to kiss her so passionately ... and possessively, and her not to experience some resultant feeling of shame. It had all seemed so natural at the time, and she supposed that Kort must have felt the same, hence his not mentioning it afterwards.

'I think it's time we made our way back.' Kort spoke softly, swinging round as he did so. 'Have you enjoyed our stroll?'

'Very much, thank you.'

He smiled down at her and her heart seemed to leap right up into her throat. This was madness! She was like a gauche schoolgirl who has suddenly found she had a crush on some man years older than herself!

'Don't thank me, Sally. I've enjoyed it too.'

They were greeted with odd glances when eventually they were back in the shed. Ray and Nicole, dancing together, came gliding up to them and Nicole asked where they had been.

'Out walking,' briefly from Kort, whose eyes were not on Nicole at all, but on the blonde woman close by who was looking at Sally as if she hated her.

'It's time I had a dance with you,' Ray was saying. 'Kort, shall we change partners?'

'If you wish.'

Nicole's eyes lit up as she slipped into Kort's arms. He towered above her and she tilted her head to look into his bronzed and handsome face. Sally frowned, and even Ray was struck by Nicole's expression.

'Is she falling for him?' he almost exploded, quite unable to believe that this could possibly happen.

'I sincerely hope not!'

'So do I! We have enough on our plates without Nicole adding to it!'

'You've spoken to Dora?'

'Yes, but I still haven't made up my mind.'

'Then it would seem that you shouldn't marry either girl,' returned Sally in crisp half angry tones.

'I'm beginning to realize that myself.'

'Well, that's something! Perhaps you'll make your confession to Nicole. Then we can both go home.'

Go home.... Like a magnet Kort drew her thoughts to himself. Never to see him again. She swallowed, aware of a tightness in her throat. Where had she been going? There was no question of anything developing between the boss and herself. The very idea was laughable.

'You want to go home?'

'It would be better all round if we left this place.' Something in her voice caught and held his attention.

'You sound depressed,' he said.

'I'm certainly not my usual bright self,' she admit-

101

ted. 'Your indecision is bad enough, but——' She broke off, scarcely aware herself of what she had meant to add to that.

'My brother,' ventured Ray slowly, leaning away from her a little. 'You don't get along very well with him, I know, and yet....'

'Yes?' Sally frowned as she spoke the one brief word.

'I find myself becoming puzzled by his attitude towards you.'

'His old flame is here tonight. He's probably trying to make her jealous.' There, it was out, and she felt better.

Ray paused a moment and then,

'It isn't like him at all. But it would seem that you are right. I myself reluctantly reached the same conclusion.'

'That he's making use of me?'

'That's a crude way of putting it, Sally,' he returned, having actually flinched at her outspokenness.

'But the correct one.'

'Yes, I believe it is.' Again he paused. 'What an unholy mess we're all in!'

'All? I myself am not in a mess——'

'Oh, but you are! It isn't any use denying that you like my brother——'

'Rubbish!' she cut in wrathfully. 'We dislike each other intensely!'

'You fight a lot, but that's nothing to go by.'

Too angry for further words, Sally gave a sigh of relief when, after what seemed an interminable silence, the music stopped and she was able to walk away from him.

However, once she was on her own, standing in a

quiet spot in the shade of a tree where she felt she was away from the scene of light and gaiety of which she had just been a part, she gave all her mind over to musing on what Ray had said. And she reached the conclusion—without much difficulty at all—that he had been right in his assertion that they were all in an 'unholy mess'.

And as if to substantiate this conclusion she suddenly heard a step close by and turned her head to look at the shadowy figure of Gracia.

'I saw you come out here,' the girl began without preamble, 'and I followed. I would like to have a talk with you.'

Her hackles well and truly up, Sally frowned at her. She had wished for a short interlude of peace, but now this girl had appeared and Sally felt she could almost have been downright rude to her and told her to go away. However, her innate good manners coming to the fore, she shrugged away her annoyance and, adopting a cordial tone and manner, politely asked Gracia what she wanted to talk about. And as Sally suspected, Gracia immediately mentioned Kort.

'Is there some understanding between you and him?' Gracia added, looking curiously at her in the dim light.

Sally computed swiftly and decided that she neither wanted to let Kort down, nor did she want to lie. She took the only other course open to her, saying quietly but firmly that she did not wish to enter on any discussion of such a subject.

'Kort would not want me to do so,' she continued, but then she added, simply because she knew it would be expected of her, 'Why do you ask? Can it be of some special interest to you?'

The girl moved uneasily.

'I might as well be honest,' she said at last, 'Kort was once in love with me——' She broke off as a small gasp escaped Sally. 'I suppose you're thinking I shouldn't mention such a thing? Well, it doesn't really matter; everyone knows about it—and about Kort's being so upset when I married someone else. He's never even looked at another woman since....' A long pause followed and Sally gained the impression that the girl was carefully searching for words. At length she continued, 'I'm a widow now and have come to visit my father. I had hoped—hoped....' Again she tailed off and Sally finished the sentence for her,

'... that you and he could pick up where you broke off?'

Gracia nodded; she was deep in thought and Sally wished there were more light, so that she could read her expression. For the girl might just care for Kort, might long since have discovered that her marriage was a mistake.

'Yes, I had hoped for a reconciliation,' murmured Gracia, seemingly unconscious of the fact that she might be talking to a girl whom Kort had already decided to marry. 'I didn't expect to see him with another girl.' Her voice caught; instinctively Sally knew that the girl's dejection was genuine, that she was hurt by the fact of Kort's bringing Sally to the dance. Gracia had obviously expected to be able to claim his whole attention, whereas she had not claimed any at all. Not only had Kort avoided dancing with her, but he had also treated her with the sort of cool indifference he might have shown to any casual acquaintance. No wonder the girl was feeling bitterly disappointed at the way things had turned out. 'I'd

104

like to know how you came to be a guest at Grey River Downs?'

It was a question; Sally immediately shook her head.

'I've no intention of discussing my private affairs,' she said, and added, 'If you'll excuse me, I must go back——'

'All right! If you won't talk of yourself perhaps you'll talk about Nicole? How does she come to be here? Is there something between her and Ray? I'm interested because it's been known for years and years that Ray would eventually marry another girl.'

A heavy frown had already settled on Sally's wide forehead.

'If you want information concerning Ray,' she said stiffly, 'then you must approach him directly.'

It was Gracia's turn to frown.

'There seems to be more than one mystery! There must be, because if all was open and above board you wouldn't be so reluctant to talk to me.' She paused, half expecting Sally to make some remark, but she merely shrugged her shoulders impatiently. 'It's rather stupid, really,' continued Gracia at length, 'because I've only to ask someone else about Ray and Nicole.'

'Then do just that,' advised Sally crisply. 'I'm sorry, but I must go,' she added, and twisted round abruptly before the other girl could find anything further to say.

Gracia made no attempt to accompany her, and when on reaching the shed Sally turned to look back there was no sign of the girl. Where had she gone? wondered Sally vaguely. Perhaps she was staying out there for a while, desiring her own company rather than that of the gay crowd who were laughing and dancing in the shed.

'Where have you been?' demanded Nicole, immediately coming up to Sally. 'I missed you....' Her voice broke a little and, with swift insight, Sally took her arm and led her on to the verandah. 'It's Ray,' whispered Nicole huskily. 'He's been with that horrid Dora more than he's been with me!'

'Not more, dear——'

'Yes, he has! And I've been talking to Robert and he's told me that Ray and Dora have had an understanding for a long time.' She was almost in tears, and with a swift rise of anger Sally could have gone to Ray there and then and demanded to know whether or not he had made up his mind. However, she refrained, naturally, and concentrated on trying to comfort Nicole.

'I shouldn't take any notice of gossip, Nicole,' she said soothingly. 'Who is this Robert, anyway?'

'He arrived very late. He's the son of Mr Gilmer—you know, the gentleman we were introduced to not long after we arrived. Kort didn't say who he was, but Ray's told me that he's a tour operator. He organizes trips into the interior.'

'To Alice Springs?'

'Yes, that's right. Well, Robert's his younger son. He's at college in Brisbane, but he's on holiday at present. That's why he's here.'

Sally looked hard at her.

'He's the tall young man you've been dancing with when Ray was with Dora?'

Nicole nodded her head.

'I think he likes me, but I want Ray....' Her voice trailed away to silence as Kort passed the open window, dancing with his host's married daughter.

Nicole seemed mesmerised by him.

'I told you not to complicate matters by having a crush on Kort.'

Nicole turned, colouring deeply.

'If I can't have Ray then I'm sure I don't want his brother,' she returned pettishly. 'I don't know what makes you think I've a crush on him!'

'Nicole dear,' said Sally in soft and gentle tones, 'what would you say if I suggested we go home?'

To her surprise no swift protest leapt to her companion's lips.

'I couldn't make a decision without thinking about it.'

'But you feel that things haven't gone the way you expected?'

'They haven't—no. Ray's undecided.'

'And so are you, pet.'

Nicole nodded forlornly.

'I admit it. But I do like Ray a lot,' she added hastily. 'I feel we could have hit it off very well indeed.'

'You like him ... but you don't love him. Well, Nicole, liking just isn't enough.' Sally paused a moment, her eyes following the magnificent figure of Kort as he seemed to glide, with his partner, around the room. He had on a very light grey tropical suit, with a snow-white shirt which contrasted with remarkable attactiveness with his bronzed skin. He seemed to stand out from all the rest of the men present, and as her eyes wandered to where a group of young ladies stood she saw that every eye was following him. There were some very beautiful girls present here tonight and Sally did wonder how so eligible a bachelor had managed to retain his freedom for so long. 'I'm going to ask you to consider my suggestion that we leave and return to England.'

A silence followed; glancing at her foster-sister, Sally saw her lips quiver. But as always Nicole was able to summon her innate common sense and presently she said,

'I'll seriously consider it, Sally. I must admit that we're not getting very far like this. I suspected Ray of being undecided when he changed his mind about taking me to his own place.'

'You don't seem to have any resentment at all against Kort.'

'My feelings with regard to him are awfully mixed, Sally. He's so handsome and arresting that I feel I could never dislike him no matter what he did. I'm sure that he's only thinking of his brother's future.'

Sally said nothing. It was plain that although Nicole had been made unhappy by the attention which Ray was giving to the other girl, she was certainly not heartbroken, which meant that although she had firmly stated that she was in love with Ray, she had not really been sure about this.

No more was said, as Ray appeared, smiling thinly and asking Nicole to dance.

Left to her own thoughts, Sally found herself a seat on the verandah and tried to relax. But the more she thought about leaving Australia the more dejected did she become. She had started out with such optimism despite the conviction that there would be many difficulties—most of which she felt would be attributd to the arrogant brother of the man whose invitation had brought Nicole and herself to Grey River Downs. She had anticipated some sightseeing, had concluded she would learn a little about the people and the country.

Instead, right from the start she had been enmeshed in a web of doubts and difficulties.

And it was not just anxiety for Nicole that was troubling her at this present time. It was her own unrest, her dawning knowledge that, deep down in her subconscious, she was concealing something ... shirking an analysis of her own mind.

Kort.... His kiss had been the most exciting experience she had ever known. Other men had kissed her—Paul and she had been going about together for almost a year, so naturally he had kissed her—but never had she known the kind of thrill which Kort had been able to give her. Why had he kissed her? Was it merely the atmosphere, out there, in the silence and the starlit coolness of an Australian night? Was it a casual act, which would have happened no matter what girl he had been with? At this thought Sally frowned, and felt the blood rush to her face. She knew she would like to think that it was her he had wanted to kiss, yet paradoxically she was accepting the fact that she was merely an acquaintance in his eyes, and, moreover, one whom he intended using in order to make Gracia jealous. Or it could be that he had no desire to make her jealous, but merely to let her know that his interest in her was no longer alive. In either case he was using Sally, and she could not understand why she felt so little resentment. She should by rights have been fuming, and ready to confront him with the information that she knew exactly what he was about.

'All alone ...?' Softly came the voice, heard above the music only by virtue of its clarity and precise modulation. She glanced up, conscious of a fluttering in the region of her heart.

'I was just having a few minutes by myself,' she

murmured, a smile curving her lips.

'And I broke in on your reverie.' Kort casually drew forward a chair and sat down. There was a quality of satire in his tone as he added, turning his head to regard her lovely profile, 'Private thoughts—or do you want to talk?'

She gave him a puzzled glance.

'I don't know what you mean?'

'I saw Gracia approaching you out there.'

Startled, Sally could only murmur a brief, 'Well?'

'She had a reason for wanting to talk to you, obviously.' He paused reflectively; his eyes, grave and dark, were vacantly fixed on some point beyond the low fence of the saddling paddock. He seemed a million miles away and she knew instinctively that he had cast off the years and was young again ... and in love with the beautiful Gracia. Looking at him, and vitally aware of his attractions as a man, Sally was amazed that any girl, having won his love, could throw him over for another man. True, his nature was such that arrogance and dominance were a part of him, but, as Sally had suspected right at the beginning, there was something contradictory to his character. She was now sure there was a gentler side to him, but she rather thought that two women only had seen it—his mother and Gracia. 'Would you care to tell me what she said?' Kort spoke at last, and a moment of uneasy silence followed his words.

'It's difficult,' began Sally with undisguised reluctance. 'I——'

'Don't worry that you'll either offend or surprise me,' he interrupted quietly. 'I already have a very good idea what she talked to you about.' Sally said nothing, hoping he himself would continue, and this he did. 'She told you that she and I were once engaged?' Half statement, half question, and again Sally remained silent, amazed that the superior boss of Grey River Downs would unbend to this extent. There must be a good reason for it, but try as she would Sally could not discover it.

'She wanted to know whether there was—an—an understanding between you and me,' Sally told him at last, and he nodded slowly, his eyes once again becoming vacant. Sally herself felt exceedingly embarrassed, and looked away. But Kort's voice very quickly brought her attention to him again.

'And what did you tell her, Sally?'

She stared at him in astonishment, totally confused by this strange manner he was adopting.

'What would you have expected me to tell her?' she challenged curiously.

'The obvious answer would have been for you to offer an emphatic denial....' A pause, and then, slowly, his eyes never leaving her face, 'But you didn't deny it, did you?' he said.

Dazedly she shook her head.

'How do you know?' she asked.

A faint smile touched his lips, and his eyes took on a quizzical expression.

'Because you didn't want to destroy the impression which I myself had been trying to give.' The total frankness of this only served to increase Sally's astonishment.

'I wish I understood you,' she returned impatiently. 'It seems to me that you're having fun at the expense of both of us!'

'Fun?' The raising of his brows instantly dispelled

the idea she had formed. He shook his head. 'I can assure you it isn't amusing.' He did not expand on this but said curiously, 'Just what did you say to her, Sally?'

'I said I didn't intend to enter into any discussion of a subject such as that.'

'So....' The shaft of an amused smile hovered fleetingly on his lips. 'I was right, then, in my conviction that you would hesitate about destroying the impression which I'd wanted to give?'

She frowned at him, feeling he was inwardly triumphant, because she had decided not to embarrass him.

'I can still tell her the truth,' she almost snapped.

'But you won't,' he responded with confidence. As she could not contradict him she said nothing, and after a few thoughtful, and undecided, moments, Kort spoke again, once more surprising her by the frank and open manner he was adopting towards her. All his high-handed hauteur seemed to have dissolved completely—in fact, his customary reserve had also disappeared, and he spoke as if to a confidant. 'As my preference is for complete freedom, it goes without saying that I shall never marry. Gracia had hopes—I knew this even before she returned to her father's house. The way I chose was one which would cause her little or no embarrassment. She'll now go back to Sydney immediately and settle down in the house her late husband left her.'

Unemotional the voice; he seemed austere suddenly, and incalculable. 'I must thank you for assisting me,' he added, but there was a total absence of gratitude in his voice. It was as though he took for granted her co-operation in his scheme. Sally's instinct was to produce some acid retort to this blatant confidence but, strangely, she desisted, unwilling to create friction between them. She said after some thought,

'I don't think Mrs Lester will leave for Sydney yet a while.'

Kort raised his brows.

'Oh . . . why?'

A slight hesitation and then,

'Her attitude didn't strike me as one of total resignation,' she ventured at last, her manner one of faint apology as she added, 'Perhaps I shouldn't be forming opinions about something which doesn't concern me?'

'It's only natural that you should have formed some sort of opinion about the whole affair.' He regarded her with a curious expression. 'I'd like to know why you've decided that Gracia is not totally resigned.'

Sally looked at him. She was becoming even more puzzled by his attitude towards her. He had become so free and easy, speaking as if they had always enjoyed a friendly relationship rather than one of near enemies.

'I don't think I can explain,' she had to confess. 'It was just that she seemed puzzled; she isn't convinced that there's—er—anything serious between you and me. . . .' Her voice faded and she looked away, a slight frown creasing her brow. She was uncomfortable and she wanted nothing more than to bring this conversation to a speedy end. 'I expect time will prove me to be right or wrong,' she said, before deliberately changing the subject, commenting on the party itself and the meticulous care with which the arrangements had been made.

'They've taken so much trouble to see that everything is perfect,' she commented appreciatively, her

113

eyes moving from the pretty lanterns above her head to the long tables still loaded with delicious food.

Kort eyed her perceptively, fully aware of her reason for changing the subject.

'It's customary for us to go to a great deal of trouble when giving a party,' he said casually. 'Our friends expect it of us.' He stopped, and glanced up. Gracia's father had come quietly up to them and he spoke at once, his voice faintly anxious.

'Have you seen Gracia, Kort?'

Kort frowned in puzzlement.

'What do you mean? She's about somewhere.'

Gracia's father was shaking his head.

'I've been looking for her, as I think it's time we were leaving, but I can't find her anywhere.'

'She was with me a short while ago—out there——' Sally flicked a hand, indicating the dark region beyond the area illuminated by the lights from the barn. 'She stayed when I came away. I had the impression that she wanted to be alone.'

The girl's father looked worried.

'She's been strange tonight,' he murmured, almost to himself. 'I'll go and see if I can find her.'

'I'll come with you,' said Kort at once. 'She can't be far away.'

CHAPTER SEVEN

TEN minutes later the two men returned, coming straight to Sally, who was still where they had left her.

'Where exactly did you leave Gracia?' demanded the girl's father before Kort had the chance to speak. 'It surely couldn't have been far from here?'

'No, it wasn't——'

'Did she just stay there?' intervened Kort, 'or did she walk away in the other direction?'

'Is she lost?' Sally looked up into Kort's set face, aware of a growing apprehension within her.

'We haven't seen her,' answered Kort in troubled tones. 'We've just been speaking to John Rossiter and she hasn't returned to the barn.'

'Do you think she would have gone for a walk——?' Sally stopped, and shook her head. 'She'd have more sense than to wander off, away from the lights——' Again she stopped, glancing around and making a silent calculation as to how far anyone would have to go before losing sight of the lights. There was also the music, which was blaring forth from the open windows of the shed; that music would surely be heard for a great distance. 'She can't be lost,' added Sally with conviction. 'The lights——'

'She *is* lost!' snapped the girl's father. 'Kort, we must organize a search party!'

An hour later there was still no sign of Gracia. The dancing had ceased and everyone was out looking for her. For some absurd reason Sally felt guilty, as if she alone were the cause of Gracia's being lost. The attitude of the girl's father did not help, since he had remarked more than once that it was a pity that Sally had not mentioned to someone the fact of Gracia's having remained out there on her own.

Sally later heard him telling Kort that Gracia had been upset all the evening, and that he now wished he had suggested taking her home much earlier.

'I don't think she expected you to give her the cold shoulder the way you did,' he added bluntly, and Sally would have liked to hear Kort's response, but she turned away, joining Nicole and Ray as they went off to search along the bank of the creek. It had already been searched, of course, but by now there was concern that Gracia might be lying unconscious somewhere, and as the vegetation along the banks of the creek was naturally thicker than anywhere else, it was decided to make a more thorough search. Others were already there, moving about, torches in their hands.

'I can't think how she could come to be lost, Sally.' This was from Nicole, who was by Sally's side, Ray having joined two other men who were crossing the dry creek bed, making for a little island formed by an abandoned meander. 'You'd have to go for miles before you'd get away from all the lights.'

'I'm as puzzled as you,' returned Sally. 'I think she must have had some sort of accident and lost consciousness, just as is now feared.'

'It's the only explanation, isn't it?'

Sally nodded, but she was extremely puzzled, the main reason being that so little time had elapsed between her leaving Gracia and the appearance of the girl's father with the information that she was missing.

116

Gracia could not possibly have travelled far, and if that were the case why hadn't she been found? It seemed that every inch of ground had been covered, since there were dozens of people taking part in the search.

A short while later there was a shout from Kort. He had found Gracia lying unconscious at the foot of a tree, her body almost hidden by the tall porcupine grass. By this time the cars and utilities were out; Kort carried Gracia to one of these and she was driven to the Rossiter homestead.

'My—my h-head....' Gracia shuddered as if at some unpleasant recollection. 'I fell—against a tree....' Her eyes roved slowly around those who were gathered about her. They found Kort's face, then shadowed. Watching him, Sally noticed the severity of his mouth, but otherwise his face was an expressionless mask. Nevertheless, she sensed the deep anxiety which had possessed him during the search. Perhaps he was blaming himself for what had happened, admitting that the girl, repulsed by his coldly unemotional manner towards her, had been so unhappy that she had wandered off on her own and then met with the accident. 'I'm sorry for—for all th-the trouble....' Again she shuddered, and put a hand to her head. One of the guests was a doctor, but it was not until five minutes later that he arrived at the homestead, having been driving his utility when some-one hailed him, telling him that Gracia had been found.

Watching his face as he bent to examine Gracia's head, Sally saw him frown, as if in puzzlement.

'Your head struck a tree?' he said, his deep-set grey eyes looking directly into Gracia's. 'There doesn't appear to be any swelling.'

117

The girl made no answer, merely turning into the pillow and wincing with pain as she did so. The doctor shrugged, nonplussed. When Gracia's father asked if it were safe to move her he paused momentarily, then said yes, it was quite safe to take her home.

The following day Kort was in touch with Gracia's father over the air. He later told Sally that Gracia was now fully recovered.

'I'm glad,' she said, recalling the wave of relief that had swept through her when Gracia was found. 'I somehow felt it was partly my fault that she'd gone off like that.'

'Your fault?' frowned Kort, looking interrogatingly at her.

She nodded her head thoughtfully.

'I hadn't been altogether nice to her,' she reminded him. 'Also, in the light of what happened later I felt I shouldn't have left her out there on her own.'

Kort's frown deepened.

'There was no reason why you should have stayed with her.'

'No ... but I think now that I should have made sure she was returning to the shed. She wasn't very happy, you see.'

Kort merely shrugged his shoulders.

'That wasn't your fault, Sally,' he assured her. 'Gracia has only herself to blame for the way she's feeling at this present time.'

Something in his tone and in his glance brought an inexplicable little access of uneasiness to her. Deliberately she thrust away the questions which followed hard upon this uneasiness, but she was unable to ignore the fact that she was becoming increasingly aware of his inordinate attractions, not least of which was the remarkably noble and superior bearing he adopted at all times. His physical attractions were always evident, no matter whether he was dressed in denims, as now, or in immaculate evening attire.

His horse was brought; he hesitated a moment, then asked her if she were intending to ride. Common sense warned her to say no; instead she said yes, and Kort requested that her horse should be saddled and brought to her.

They rode together towards the wide valley where the mob of cattle grazed.

'We'll join them for smoko,' said Kort, turning to Sally with a smile. 'Are you ready for a gallop?'

'Of course.'

Some of the men watched their approach with interest. Sally could imagine their surprise that the boss should ride with a woman by his side.

They sat by the creek, under the shade of a eucalypt, a little distance from where the men were squatting, drinking billy tea and chatting together. Kort, however, was obviously not in a talkative mood, since he made no attempt to open up a conversation with Sally. She herself was content to remain silent, her dreamy gaze on the sun-hazed outline of the mountains. Between them and the valley the landscape was flat for the most part, but relieved here and there by a small hillock, relic of some ancient height long since worn away by the machinations of weather and time. Along the edge of the distant billabong eucalypts formed dark shadows and it was not difficult to imagine kangaroos feeding in the high grasses which flourished there.

'It's all so peaceful—and vast.' Sally spoke at length, voicing her thoughts; her companion turned his head to look at her.

'I must admit that your attitude towards the Outback surprises me,' he said.

'You didn't think I'd like it?'

'I certainly didn't expect you to be so enthusiastic about it,' he owned.

'I don't see how anyone could not be enthusiastic about it,' said Sally, her pensive gaze once again fixed upon the outline of the mountains.

'You could ... settle here?' Soft the tone; it had a note of hesitancy about it, as if Kort had not fully understood why he should have uttered such words. 'You'll have to come back for a holiday some time.'

Sally shook her head.

'I'd never have the money for that.'

Kort raised a slender brown hand to suppress a yawn. His eyes, narrowed against the fierce reflection of the sun on the hills, were roving the landscape around him. Sally could guess at his thoughts, could imagine his thinking that all this would one day come to his brother and, therefore, Ray must have a wife whose social standing here was already established. Well, it would seem that Nicole was almost ready to return home, resigned to the fact that she was not for Ray. Sally said, in a rather grave tone,

'Nicole and I might be leaving quite soon.'

Kort's face came round; the sunlight was full upon it, accentuating the clarity of the features and the tinges of grey at the temples. Sally caught her breath; his attractions at this moment were considerable.

'This is sudden, isn't it?' A slight pause and then, 'The result of Ray's paying so much attention to Dora at the dance?'

'Probably. But Nicole hasn't said, definitely, that

she wants to go home. She said she would consider it.'

Kort's gaze became perceptive.

'You yourself asked her to consider returning to England?'

She nodded.

'I did, yes. It seems to me that Ray shouldn't marry either girl, simply because he doesn't know his own mind. He's so confused that in my opinion he should go to his own ranch and try to discover which one he loves.'

'Love....' mused Kort, ignoring the rest of what Sally had said. 'Why do women attach so much importance to so trivial a matter?'

She turned impatiently; he saw the frown on her lovely face and smiled sardonically, as if he were deriving satisfaction from the knowledge that he could make her angry.

'You're so cynical!' she snapped.

'I'm realistic. Dreams and flights of fancy are not for me.'

'Love is real!'

'A figment of the female imagination.'

'Oh....' She quivered with anger. 'You tempt me to remind you of something——' She stopped, not daring to venture any further, but, strangely, he laughed and said,

'Of my callow youth? Don't you see that I'm attempting to protect my brother from such folly?— that I'm endeavouring to have him benefit from my mistakes?'

She sighed exasperatedly.

'You're impossible!' she said, and picked up her tea. 'Such obstinacy is something I can't understand.'

His eyes glimmered with sudden mirth.

'It's just like a woman to talk in that vein. Simply because you've failed to make your point you call me obstinate.'

Sally said nothing and after a moment he reverted to the question of Nicole, making the comment that she had obviously reached the stage where she was willing to admit that her action in coming here had been impetuous.

'It was no such thing,' retorted Sally, unwilling to cede him even the smallest point. 'On the contrary, it was a wise decision; both she and Ray had to find out whether or not they were suited.'

'And they've discovered that they're not.' A statement, spoken mechanically and yet with conviction. 'When do you think you'll be leaving?'

Her heart seemed to drag suddenly. So casual his tones; he wanted nothing more than to see the back of both Nicole and herself. She thought of that unguarded interlude when she had let him kiss her—when she had responded to his kisses without any attempt at restraint—and she blushed inwardly, wishing she could re-live those moments, to be given the opportunity of coldly repelling him. He was speaking again, repeating what he had already said.

'As I've already mentioned, Nicole hasn't definitely made up her mind.'

'But you're quite sure that she'll give up the idea of marrying Ray.' Another statement, and this time Sally found herself saying,

'Yes, I feel quite sure that she'll give up the idea of marrying him.'

Kort seemed to draw a deep breath, a manifestation of his relief. Sally looked at him, into the sun-tanned toughness of his face. She noted the lines of strength, noted the depth of expression in his eyes ... and she knew that he had been right from the very first: Nicole was not the girl for Ray.

It was three days later that Nicole came to Sally and said she had made her decision.

'We've talked and talked, and reached the conclusion that we're not suited.' There was a certain sadness in Nicole's voice, and an element of disappointment. 'It's a shame, really,' she went on, her eyes wandering over the wide spinifex plain to the distant massif, gleaming like gold as its peaks reflected the brilliant afternoon sunshine, 'because I love it here.'

'So do I.' Sally spoke automatically, dwelling on the life she could live if only it were possible for her to remain here. The utter peace, the remoteness of the Outback from all the hustle and bustle of the town in which she had been obliged to work—and where she must soon be working again. There was of course the possibility of obtaining a post in one of the households here, but she knew instinctively that such a move on her part would be one which would be regarded by Kort with extreme disapproval.

And the last thing she wanted was to earn his disapproval. ...

'Well,' sighed Nicole, 'it just wasn't to be. There's one consolation: Mum will be glad.'

'She would have missed you, certainly, but she wanted only what would make you happy.'

Nicole nodded her head.

'When shall we go, Sally?'

'You'd like to go soon?' Sally turned away, swallowing hard. She was wishing she had never come here, had never met Kort Lander....

'I can't see any advantage in staying, not now I've made up my mind.'

Sally nodded her head, turning again to look at Nicole, and surprised to note that her face reflected eagerness, as if she were now actually impatient to be gone from Grey River Downs just as quickly as she could.

'I'll tell Kort, and he'll arrange everything for us.'

'It's Ray's responsibility, but he'll obviously leave it all to his brother.' Nicole's voice faded slowly, and her eyes became pensive. 'Kort's so reliable, so strong. Why is he so different from Ray?'

'He's older, for one thing.' Sally's eyes searched; she would always wonder if Nicole had had a crush on the boss of Grey River Downs.

'Yes—a lot older....'

'And a confirmed bachelor,' supplemented Sally just for good measure.

Nicole looked swiftly at her.

'I like him, but I'm not in love with him, if that's what you're thinking!'

'I'm relieved to hear it,' returned Sally. 'I must admit that at one time you had me a little worried.'

'I know I did....' Nicole paused in thought. 'I think I could have fallen for him, but I knew it was no use. Kort would never look at me in *that* particular way.'

'Nor at any other woman.'

'It's very strange to me. He's so handsome—could have anyone he wanted.'

'His cattle station's all he wants. He lives for it.'

'Which, to my mind, is silly!'

'You think he ought to be married?'

'Of course. And have a son. Why should poor Ray have to inherit something he doesn't really want?'

'Perhaps Kort will change his attitude one day.'

'And get married? Ray was hoping he and his old flame would get together again at the dance. He was terribly disappointed at the way Kort treated her.'

'I don't think Gracia is right for Kort,' returned Sally quietly, and out from nowhere drifted the recollection of Kort's kisses, and the protective feel of his arms about her. Words rose in her throat, but she did not allow herself to say them, words springing from the deep recesses of her mind, words that would reveal with stark reality what her consciousness strove to suppress. It was Nicole who voiced them, staggering Sally and making her wonder if the girl was a mind-reader.

'I think *you* are right for Kort.'

'You——!' Sally's cheeks coloured and she glanced away. 'What a thing to say, Nicole!'

'You and he looked so perfect at the dance—so well matched, if you know what I mean?' Nicole spoke reflectively, bypassing her foster-sister's embarrassed exclamation. 'It's a wonder you haven't fallen for him. I know I would have done so had he given me the attention he gave to you—and it lasted all the evening. He did dance with one or two others, it's true,' went on Nicole, still in the same reflective mood, 'but you were the one he was with the most.'

Sally changed the subject, reverting to the question of their departure from Australia.

'We haven't seen much of the country, have we?' Nicole's voice held a hint of regret. 'I'd have liked to see Alice Springs, at least.'

'Never mind. It's been quite an experience.'

'It's been a waste and you know it. You've given up

your job and——'

'I've had the trip out here, Nicole, so I'm very fortunate indeed. Let's not dwell on what might have been.'

'I fully expected Ray to take us about.'

'Don't look so dejected, pet! There's nothing lost—not really.'

'You're so generous and understanding, Sally. But I know that you're just as disappointed as I that we haven't been anywhere.'

'We've seen the Outback, and a town.'

Nicole frowned.

'That's not much to come all this way for!'

'We didn't come for a holiday, love.'

'No. . . .' A long pause and then, 'Will you talk to Kort immediately he comes in? I want to leave as soon as possible.'

Sally nodded silently, and that evening after dinner she told Kort that they wanted to leave.

He nodded with satisfaction, but instantly frowned when Sally added that Nicole wanted to go at once.

'At once?' he repeated sharply. 'Surely there's no real urgency?'

Her heart gave a little jerk. It would seem that Kort was not so eager to see the back of her as she had imagined.

'I—well——'

'You haven't seen anything,' he went on, reflecting what Nicole had already said. 'You ought to visit Alice Springs. Everyone who comes to the Outback does that particular trip.'

'That would be wonderful,' she breathed, totally unaware of the glow in her eyes, as they looked up into his. There was a profound moment of silence before Kort said, his tone becomeing unexpectedly abrupt,

'Ray will fly you both there.'

'Ray...?' Sally had taken it for granted that Kort had himself meant to fly them to Alice Springs. 'Er— yes,' she murmured, hoping her disappointment was not apparent. 'However, I must consult Nicole. She seems anxious to leave at once, now that she and Ray have decided they won't marry.'

'There's no need to run off like that.' Kort's tones were suddenly imperious—dictatorial, almost. 'You must both stay on for a while as my guests.'

Must.... It was an order—a very firm and definite order. Sally looked at him, a question in her eyes. What was the reason for his invitation? He was not in the least interested in Nicole.... He looked down at her, impassively, ignoring her silent question.

'I'll speak with Nicole,' she promised.

'Good.' Kort glanced at his watch. 'Care for a stroll?' he asked.

Sally found herself trembling with excitement, but she managed to assume a cool and impersonal manner as she replied,

'That would be nice. I love the air when the sun's gone down.'

'Cool and fresh. It blows across the plain from the mountains.'

They strolled away into the darkness. The moon was almost full, and the sky filled with stars. Total solitude prevailed over the vast silent spaces which, eons ago, had been the bed of an ancient sea.

'If only one could imagine what it was once like...?' Sally spoke absently, and to herself, but of course her words were caught by her companion.

'This land, you mean?'

She nodded, looking up at him and smiling ruefully.

'I was thinking of ancient times—fifty million years ago.'

'You *have* been doing your homework, haven't you?' He had said this before, but now his astonishment was most pronounced.

'I'm interested in the land, and its formation,' she returned, although a little diffidently. 'It's a difficult subject, but one can gather a few facts if one tries hard enough.'

'And you've gathered that this land here is an old sea-bed?'

'That's right. And the eroded ranges were islands.'

'Very good,' he commended. 'And what about our climate?'

'Oh, I know it's very varied, simply because you have latitudes from the south-east trade winds to the roaring forties.'

Kort laughed, but again praised her knowledge.

'It's strange how many people travel to a country and never learn a thing about it beforehand,' he added, slowing down his pace on realizing suddenly that she was having to skip now and then to keep up with his long easy strides.

'Yes, but for me it's very necessary that I know about the places I visit.'

'It makes it all more interesting, eh?'

'Of course.'

A silence fell between them. Sally thought of the animosity which had at first characterized their relationship. She had branded him pompous and self-opinionated, vowing to champion Nicole and Ray if it so happened that they wanted to marry and Kort attempted to prevent them from doing so. Well, many changes had come about since then. Kort and she were no longer enemies—on the contrary, they had become friends, for surely only friends could be strolling along like this, in the moonlit solitude and silence of the evening.

A little sigh escaped her, a sigh of contentment ... and yet there was a restlessness about her, which was natural, for she knew she wanted nothing more than that Kort should stop—perhaps over there, where the red river gums fringed the creek—and take her in his arms, just as he had done at the dance.... She could feel the hard pressure of his lips, could think back with wonderment at her own ready response.

'You've gone quiet.' Kort slowed down, and sent her a slanting glance. 'What are you thinking, Sally?'

She swallowed and shook her head.

'I was just enjoying the stroll,' she replied, managing to inject a casual note into her voice. 'It's pleasant to come out, knowing one is safe.'

'Safe?'

'Well, you said I mustn't walk far on my own.'

'Yes, I did. You've already seen the trouble which can be caused when someone gets lost.'

'And I'm told by Ray that there are wild bulls about.'

'Scrubs, yes; they can be very dangerous. However, they rarely come as close to the homestead as this.'

Another silence, which lasted five minutes or more, and then Kort said it was time they returned to the house.

But when they reached it Kort seemed reluctant to enter. He stood on the verandah, looking out towards the pale horizon against which moving silhouettes betrayed the presence of cattle, and of the slow-spoken, suntanned stockmen who vigilantly rode among them.

'I'll say good night.' It was Sally who broke the silence at last, speaking softly because it did seem that Kort's reverie should not be disturbed. He turned slowly, and looked down into her face, his eyes all-examining as they moved from her shining hair to her wide forehead and then down to her softly-parted lips.

Suddenly he moved, to bend his head; she held her breath, her pulses racing as she waited for his kiss. A few seconds elapsed, and then he straightened up.

'Good night,' he said abruptly. 'Sleep well.'

CHAPTER EIGHT

To Sally's surprise Nicole raised no objection whatsoever to staying on as Kort's guest. On the contrary, she seemed to welcome the idea. Frowning in puzzlement, Sally reminded her that she had been eager to leave at the first opportunity.

'Yes, I know,' murmured Nicole after a moment of hesitation. 'But. . . .' She trailed off slowly, and turned away, avoiding Sally's interrogating gaze. 'Robert called this morning, and—and we chatted together for a long while.'

Sally's frown deepened.

'Well?'

Nicole shrugged uncomfortably.

'He asked me not to leave yet awhile,' she said, and an astounded silence followed.

'You mean,' ejaculated Sally at last, 'that you're now falling for Robert!'

'I know it sounds silly——'

'Darned silly! Nicole, where is your common sense? First it's Ray, then Kort——'

'No, not Kort—never!'

'You've admitted you could have fallen in love with him had you thought there was any chance of his reciprocating.' Sally was vexed and she made no attempt to conceal the fact. 'Now it's this Robert—whom you've met only once!'

'Twice.'

Exasperatedly Sally drew a breath.

'I think we'd better leave here immediately,' she decided. For although she herself wanted more than anything to stay, her first duty was to her foster-mother who was relying on her to see that her daughter came to no harm. 'I'll tell Kort to make the necessary arrangements.'

Would he raise objections? she wondered, recalling his imperious manner as he told her to persuade Nicole to remain at the ranch. Well, it would make no difference, because she, Sally, was not intending to take chances where Nicole was concerned.

'I'm staying.' The quiet words fell on the silence and Sally looked up, amazed.

'You can't——'

'Both Ray and I have listened to others, and in consequence we've not been able to think for ourselves. Ray's been so confused, and I've been upset about it. I took the advice given by both you and Kort, but it was against my own inclinations——'

'But you now accept it as good advice,' interrupted Sally, hurt by the way Nicole was speaking to her.

'No, I'm not so sure that I do,' was Nicole's surprising answer. 'I believe that Ray and I could have managed far better had we been left alone. We like each other, even now, and we once were sure we were in love.'

'Ray was never sure; you know very well he wasn't.'

'He cared more for me than Dora. And I'll tell you this,' added Nicole, pointing a finger at her, 'Ray won't ever marry Dora—so Kort's in for a disappointment!'

'I rather thought he wouldn't marry Dora,' returned Sally calmly. 'I myself told him he shouldn't consider marrying either of you.'

Nicole shrugged her shoulders. She seemed to have grown up within the past few hours.

'I've promised Robert I'll not go home yet,' she said. 'On Thursday he's taking me to a town called Pedamooka, where there's a festival. We're going in his plane.'

Sally stared disbelievingly at her.

'You promised that, knowing you'd asked me to see Kort about going home?'

'We shall be going home, but not yet.' She paused but added, when Sally did not speak, 'It's rather accommodating of Kort to invite us to stay. It's saved my asking him if we can.'

'I just don't understand you,' returned Sally angrily. 'What in the name of heaven can come of this affair with Robert?'

'Perhaps nothing ... perhaps something.'

'You're quite determined to stay?'

'Quite. I'm sorry,' she added, biting her lip. 'I hate to go against your wishes, Sally, but this time I must follow my own inclinations.' Again she paused and then, as the thought occurred to her, 'Do you yourself really want to go home yet? You've just asked me if I want to stay, remember?'

'Because Kort wants us to do so.'

'Why?' queried Nicole curiously.

'He thinks we ought to see something of the Centre—says we must visit Alice Springs.'

'He does?' Nicole's eyes glowed. 'Isn't that generous of him? I expect he's feeling that way on account of my not marrying his brother.'

'You asked if I want to go home. For myself, no, but for your well-being, yes.'

'I suppose you consider me ungrateful?' Nicole's

eyes were shadowed. 'I'm not really. It's just that I'm feeling slightly rebellious—desiring only to please myself what I do, and to make my own decisions.'

'You've made your own decisions, Nicole,' responded Sally quietly. 'Kort and I merely advised you and Ray to wait a little while before rushing into marriage. The decision to call the whole thing off was made by you—and Ray, of course.'

'True, but we were influenced, nevertheless.'

Sally looked at her closely.

'If you had your time to come over again would you rush into marriage with Ray?'

Nicole frowned, and glanced away.

'You're not being fair to me, Sally. I can't answer your question.'

Sally remained silent, thinking of the conclusion she herself had reached: that Kort was right when he said that Nicole was not the girl for Ray.

'I think I'll ride over to Kort and thank him for his invitation.' Nicole turned as she spoke, and beckoned to one of the rouseabouts. 'Will you saddle Tonka for me?'

'Of course, Miss Rotherham.'

'Are you coming too?' With a smile Nicole turned to Sally. 'I'm sorry if I've been horrid to you, but I'm sure you understand?' The charm was there, the lovely smile still hovering. Sally responded, quite unable to remain vexed with Nicole for any length of time.

'Let's forget it. I must admit I'm worried about you, though, yet on the other hand I'm honest enough to own that I want to pay that visit to Alice Springs. Dusky,' she called to the Abo rouseabout who was standing watching Nicole's horse being saddled, 'will

134

you saddle mine, please?'

'Marengo?—but of course!'

A few minutes later the two girls were cantering over the spinifex plain towards the low line of hills where the stockmen were riding about among the cattle. Kort was there, standing by a bore-trough, chatting to one of the Aborigine stockriders, and he glanced up on hearing the sound of hooves as the girls drew near.

'Something wrong?' He looked anxiously from one to the other. Sally shook her head at once.

'I've come to thank you for your invitation,' smiled Nicole, nimbly sliding from Tonka's gleaming back. 'It's kind of you to ask us to stay.'

Sally slid down too, and stood with her hand on the horse's neck.

'I want to thank you too,' she said, her slanting blue eyes raised to Kort's dark and narrowed ones. 'As Nicole says, it's kind of you to ask us to stay.' She felt shy all at once, and unsure of herself. In contrast Nicole was perfectly self-assured, still smiling as she told Kort of the coming visit to Pedamooka with Robert. Kort's eyes widened, as well they might; he looked questioningly at Sally.

'When was this date made?' he wanted to know.

'Robert called this morning,' Nicole told him casually. 'And he asked me if I'd like to attend the festival. He's coming for me in his plane and we're going straight on from here.'

'I didn't see him this morning,' frowned Kort.

'He came after you'd gone out.'

'Just to see you?' Watching him, Sally wondered if he was remembering that Robert had paid Nicole some attention on the night of the shed dance.

135

'No, he said he had come to see one of the stock-men's wives. He brought a message from his sister.' Nicole was idly scraping the toe of her shoe against a boulder, trying to dislodge some lichen from the sur-face.

'I see....' There was a distinctly sceptical edge to Kort's slow draw, and his glance darted once again to Sally, who kept her face expressionless. She knew, though, that Kort would take the first opportunity of questioning her about this business of Robert and Nicole. And she did not have long to wait, for within half a minute or so Ray had joined them and he and Nicole went off to drink billy tea with a couple of stockmen who were busy with the stove a short dis-tance away. 'Well?' said Kort briefly, and Sally again shrugged her shoulders.

'Nicole did say, at the dance, that she thought Robert liked her,' she said, her eyes following Nicole and Ray and the two horses beside which they were walking.

'It would seem,' remarked Kort sardonically, 'that your foster-sister's as fickle as the rest.'

Colouring faintly, Sally made an instant protest.

'No such thing! This affair with Robert's merely a diversion for them both. They're off to this festival together; there's nothing wrong in that.'

Kort looked squarely at her.

'I'll wager you didn't adopt this attitude when she first told you about Robert's invitation.' It was a state-ment; Sally could not argue with him and, taking advantage of her hesitancy, he added, 'I must admit I like your honesty. You never argue when you know that to do so would be insincere.' She flushed at the compliment but remained silent. Kort laughed softly in that quiet, amused way which was becoming so familiar to her of late, and his eyes moved to the young couple who were now about to sit down and join the men for smoko. 'Tell me,' he urged, 'just what was your reaction to Nicole's confession that she had transferred her affections to Robert?'

Sally's eyes flashed.

'She didn't make any such confession!'

Kort's gaze was still directed towards the couple. He said softly,

'It could be, of course, that Nicole is playing a little game with Ray.'

'What do you mean?' demanded Sally, her own eyes wandering towards the place where Ray and Nicole were sitting.

Kort turned his head and spoke in a voice which was suddenly cold.

'She could be attempting to make my brother jealous.'

Sally drew an exasperated breath.

'You seem to have forgotten that their decision was mutual. They've discussed the position and both have decided that marriage for them is not possible.'

A sceptical light entered his eyes.

'I'm not convinced——' He shook his head. 'No, not by any means.'

'You're suggesting that Nicole is lying?' she challenged hotly.

'I haven't said so——'

'You've implied it!'

He looked at her, raising his eyebrows as if admonishing her for her show of anger.

'I'm seeing this situation objectively,' he returned, a hint of steel in his voice, 'and it seems to me that

Nicole has some ulterior motive——'

'You've just said she's transferred her affections,' broke in Sally, her anger increasing. 'Now, it would appear, you've changed your mind, and you're accusing her of trickery!'

He gave a sigh and shook his head.

'What a touchy person you are, Sally! I can understand your loyalty to Nicole, but must you become as heated as this?'

'If anyone has practised trickery,' she quivered, deliberately ignoring his words, 'it's you!'

'Me?' he said, astounded.

'Yes, you! In the very beginning you allowed Ray to be with Nicole all the time. I'm of the opinion that you hoped he would find some fault with her.'

'I admit I hoped they'd both get to know one another's faults,' he said, surprising her. 'And as things have turned out it was a wise move on my part. Ray now knows that Nicole would never make him a suitable wife.'

Abruptly she swung her head away, wondering how she could ever have come to like this man. He was hard and unfeeling; he was a total stranger to sentiment—or to any other gentle emotion, for that matter. Yet at one time she had suspected him of an underlying softness, she recalled, her thoughts becoming confused, especially as, deep down inside her, she was even now experiencing regret that he and she were once again in a position of disunity.

'I wish we'd never come here,' she quivered dejectedly. 'It was a mistake right from the beginning.'

'If I'd had my way you wouldn't have come. I told Ray it was ridiculous, since I would never be convinced that a courtship by post could ever lead to a successful marriage.' He paused a moment. 'Neither were you convinced,' he added in his low unhurried accents, and she turned at that, preserving a silence, but her clear gaze telling him all he wanted to know. He nodded his head, and the trace of a smile hovered on his lips. 'We do agree on some things,' he said with a hint of satire. 'I have a feeling that we shan't part enemies; on the contrary, we shall probably become pen-friends ourselves.' His eyes glimmered with amusement but there was a reflective quality in them too. 'Are you happy with a pen in your hand, Sally, or are you one of those people who sit and chew the end, not knowing what on earth to say?'

'I can write a letter,' she said, looking into his inscrutable dark face and wondering if he were merely amusing himself at her expense. Yes, she felt sure he was, since he would never have the time to write to her. Not that she wanted him to do so; once she left Grey River Downs she wanted only to forget—forget Kort Lander and the effect his attractiveness had had upon her.

'Yes,' came Kort's quiet voice, 'I rather think you would be extraordinarily adept at writing letters.'

'Oh, what makes you so sure?' she asked, suddenly perceiving the humour in his eyes.

'Simply because you're never at a loss for words,' he answered, smiling broadly.

She coloured slightly but retained a perfect composure for all that as she flashed him the retort,

'With you—no, strangely I'm not.'

His smile progressed to laughter.

'What a nagging wife you're going to make for some unfortunate and unsuspecting man,' he said, and her eyes opened wide with angry indignation.

'What an insulting thing to say! I've a good mind to retaliate!'

'Then why don't you?' he invited softly, his eyes still filled with humour.

'I will—seeing that you've asked for it!' Nevertheless, she did pause for a moment, and had he not been regarding her with that expression of sardonic amusement she might have had second thoughts about carrying out her threat. However, goaded by his manner, she told him he would make the most abominable husband, declaring him to be arrogant, overbearing and magisterial in his dealing with those over whom he held authority. She deplored his sarcastic tongue, reminding him that sarcasm was the lowest form of wit. She denounced his high-handed interference in affairs which did not concern him, adding, after a pause for breath, that his conceit and self-esteem were so insufferable that no woman would be able to tolerate them and therefore it was fortunate for his female acquaintances that he had decided to remain a bachelor. So angry was she by this time that her voice became so choked that it was reduced to an almost indistinct murmur of disjointed sentences.

'Well, well,' drawled Kort when finally she stopped speaking, 'I ought by rights to have no self-esteem left after listening to all that. Are you usually so deplorably ill-mannered with those whose hospitality you enjoy?' So soft the tone, but brittle as newly-formed ice, and as cold.

'You asked for it,' she reminded him in defence of herself. 'You shouldn't have goaded me. It's not usual for——' She left the sentence unfinished, floundering under his prolonged repelling stare.

'For you to treat your host with such unpardonable

rudeness? Is that what you were going to say?'

Sally made no answer; she was suffering from a sense of guilt and shame that was infinitely depressing. Why, she asked herself, had she allowed Kort to drive her to such lengths? And how could she now remain at Grey River Downs as his guest? Tears gathered at the backs of her eyes and she turned her head away, so that he should not become aware of their brightness.

'If you'll excuse me,' Kort was saying in chill expressionless tones, 'I'll leave you.' And without any further words he swung upon the stallion's back and rode off across the plain to join Ray and Nicole and the stockmen.

Sally turned to watch him go, and even through her unmarshalled thoughts she was aware of his magnificence as a rider. He and the horse might have been one, so in harmony were their movements. She found herself giving a great shuddering sigh, wondering what would be the outcome of her denouncement. Surely Kort would request her immediate departure? And what of Nicole? She would naturally want to know the reason for Kort's withdrawing his invitation so soon after having extended it to them.

Her glance moved, to find Nicole. Would she be staying with Ray for a while? It seemed that she was happily engaged in conversation, and after a few moments of indecision Sally mounted Marengo and rode away. But, restless and low in spirit as she was, she felt she could not return to the homestead.

'I'll just ride,' she said. 'There's no reason why I shouldn't go further afield so long as I keep the house or the bungalows in view.'

Half an hour later she was sitting against a tree, her pensive gaze fixed on a little hopping-mouse, a rodent which Ray had said could manage almost entirely without water. For a long while she watched it and then, suddenly startled by something unseen by Sally, it was gone.

Its disappearance seemed absurdly to leave a void and she stirred restlessly. All was so silent around her —and so still. Not even the movement of a leaf along the entire bank of the creek even though a fairly thick belt of ghost gums flourished there. Strange trees they were, yet to Sally there was exquisite beauty in them, just as there was a subtle charm about the vast wilderness that was the Outback with its sombre bush and preponderance of spiky green grasses. Here was needed no evocation of values; the richness of nature was manifested everywhere—from the incandescent mountains and the valley beneath them, to the golden sun and the sapphire sky from which it shone. Tranquillity was the keynote, with not a sound to disturb the silence except perhaps the chirping of an insect in the grass. Diffused on the still clear air was the lovely perfume of wattles, their colour a symphony of grey and molten gold.

Sally's thoughts moved on, to the sunny mornings when she would be brought from her sleep by the carolling of birds and the contagious laughter of the jackos. She thought of the lovely gardens surrounding the homestead, gardens tended carefully by two proud Aborigines who seemed not to care how much time they spent so long as the result gave them the satisfaction they desired.

And finally she thought of the future, when she would once again have taken possession of her little terraced house on the edge of town, and when she would be working in an office for five days of the week.

Well, that was the lot of millions of other people, she mused. The Kort Landers of this world were merely the fortunate few.

She turned as Marengo whinneyed, and got to her feet. It was time she was returning to the house ... but still she felt unable to do so. Turning her head, she saw that the bungalows were quite plainly visible, and as a path running at right angles to the creek looked rather inviting she decided to take it.

Time passed; she had been deep in thought and suddenly she realized that her observation on the buildings had been relaxed. They were now lost to sight entirely. She turned round and began to go back, frowning slightly as she came to a place where four paths converged. Which one had she followed?

'Oh, dear! I ought to have taken more notice than I did.' Slipping from the horse's back, she bent to look for hoofmarks, but found none. Straightenng up again, she swung around, making a complete circle. It seemed impossible that she had lost all visual contact with the homestead and the many buildings which were associated with it, but she had. However, she was not unduly troubled at this time. For one thing, it was broad daylight, and for another she felt sure she had not travelled very far from the point where the buildings would be in view. The important thing was to make sure she did not wander farther and farther away, but this was no easy task and before another hour had passed she was totally disorientated. And when at last the sun began to sink towards the crest of the mountain she admitted that she was hopelessly lost in the bush.

Fear began to assail her as the sun's rays became longer and longer, fading at last to the brilliant crimson glow that precedes the onset of dusk. She tried not to think of scrub bulls, but it was impossible to discipline her mind and she saw herself being savagely gored by one of these wild creatures. She ought to sit still, and wait for help to come, she thought, but inaction being quite impossible at a time like this she rode on, not troubling to make any attempt to find a direction but merely going where the horse took her.

Eventually she stopped, deciding to have a rest, but her feet had no sooner touched the ground than Marengo, startled by the cry of a dingo piercing the silence, reared up and then bolted.

'Marengo!' called Sally frantically, the dread picture of spending the night alone in this dark wilderness flashing into her mind. 'Marengo—come back!' But all the response she received was the sound of hooves becoming fainter and fainter until at last they could be heard no more.

Hours had passed since Marengo bolted; Sally had not moved from the place where she dismounted. She was shivering with cold and her throat was parched. She had no idea of the time, but estimated it to be about midnight.

Suddenly she went taut as the sound of something heavy and awkward came from the direction of a low granite outcrop below which the spinifex grew high and thick. Her eyes dilated as the indistinct mass began to take shape in the darkness. A scrub bull....

Fear almost choking her, she crouched low, then stayed perfectly still, scarcely daring to breathe. The bull had stopped, as if aware of another living thing somewhere in close proximity. It began to snort, then its unwieldy shape moved on, breaking twigs as it progressed through the bushes. Nearer and nearer it came—just as if it sensed her exact position.

It stood to one side sniffing the air for scent of her, but being upwind it lost the scent. At one time Sally froze as the animal actually turned its ugly head to face her, and for what seemed like an age she held her breath, her hand to her mouth to suppress a scream which was welling up within her. Slowly the head turned away and she felt her body relax, though the thumping of her heart could be felt and, she thought, heard; if only the beast would go away!

In the darkness Sally could discern only the profile, and until now she had not noticed the awful smell that accompanied the animal, so great had been her fear. It smelt of rotten vegetation that was obviously clinging to its body and, being downwind of it, Sally had the full effect of it. She now began to feel sick and was so occupied in attempting to suppress this sickness that she failed to notice the animal begin to stumble even closer to her through the undergrowth. It was about four feet away when she looked up to see it with its head close to the ground and swaying from side to side. Almost paralysed with fear, she felt she must lose her senses before very long. Again her hand went to her mouth and mentally she willed the bull to stop. It did so, but faced her now, grunting and rasping its vile breath. It was so close that the sweet sickly smell of the breath could be felt on her cheek.

'Surely it can see me,' she murmured to herself, and the fear she sensed now physically shook her. Terrified, she waited for the worst, waiting for the animal to attack her, waited for the pain of the crushing weight upon her. Again it moved, and again Sally wanted to scream, but she held on and watched. Every instinct told her that she must rise and run, but she was frozen, unable to move. And then, as if by some miracle, the bull turned and passed her and made its way back to the outcrop from where it had come, edging its bulk through the thorny bushes and disappearing into the darkness.

Sally remained motionless for some time, then raised her head. Nothing to see, and no sound. She made to rise, but fear had weakened her to such an extent that several moments elapsed before she managed to sit up. Her legs and arms were scratched by the grass, the back of her hand bore the imprint of her teeth where she had bitten into it to prevent herself from screaming. However, her only emotion at this time was one of thankfulness at her escape.

Sounds came and went with the passing hours; little nocturnal creatures unwittingly caused her to jump, or to go stiff with fear. Dingoes moved in a pack against the skyline; they were a long way off, black silhouettes of evil appearance. Sally drew a deep breath of relief when eventually she saw them disappear over a rise.

Her thoughts repeatedly went to Kort, and the other people who would surely be out looking for her. And although she felt instinctively that their task was hopeless in the dark, she kept a lookout all the time, ready to call should a light come into her vision. Kort.... She dared not think of the dreaded moment when she would come face to face with him. That he would be furiously angry went without question.

'And for this to happen so soon after my unforgivable outspokenness earlier on!' She frowned at the recollection, blaming him for provoking her but ready to accept most of the blame herself. She should have had more control. It was not as if she really meant any of what she said. No, on the contrary, she had a great respect for him, for his capable management of so vast an estate, for his prowess in the saddle, for his wisdom in knowing that Nicole would never make a suitable wife for his brother.

Suddenly Sally's musings ceased and she became alert. Was that a glimmer of light, or had she imagined it? She stared into a world whose darkness was relieved only by the light of stars. Yes, it was a light! Jumping to her feet, she called as loudly as she could, her whole being quivering with relief. The light was moving and she realized it was on a vehicle of some kind. Becoming panic-stricken as she saw the light disappearing, she called again, at the same time waving her arms frantically and stumbling over the rough ground, as she directed her steps towards the light.

'It's gone....' Her whole body sagged and she started to cry. 'They'll never find me now——' She stopped as another light appeared, just a pinprick in the darkness. She called out again, lifting her arms high in the air. The light became stationary and even yet again she called, straining her lungs to the utmost. Her call was answered, but the voice was faint, coming to her from a long way off. The vehicle's rear light was visible and she saw that it too had become stationary. The smaller light was coming towards her, jerking up and down—a torch carried in someone's hand. She continued to call, her voice echoing with a sort of eerie vibration across the dark void that separated her from the person holding the torch. Again the voice answered, but it was still a great distance away. As in a trance she waited, watching the light grow stronger with the passing moments. She recognized the voice now ... Kort's. And a trembling seized her, which, she told herself, was ridiculous. What did his wrath matter so long as she had been rescued? It was a small thing to have to endure compared with those terrifying moments when the scrub bull had been so close.

'Kort!' she breathed when at last he was close enough for her to speak in her normal voice. 'Oh, *thank* you——!'

'Sally—are you all right?' No mistaking the deep anxiety in his voice, and his arm came about her shoulders. 'Marengo returned and we concluded you'd been thrown——'

'No, nothing like that,' she broke in, anxious to reassure him that she was not hurt at all. 'I just got lost—went too far and then couldn't find my way back.'

'You——!' He stopped, shining the lamp into her face. 'You got lost?' he thundered, all his concern dissolved by anger. 'After all the warnings you had——' His sentence was never finished. Taking her by the shoulders, Kort shook her unmercifully.

'You're hurting me!' she cried. 'I——'

'Hurting you!' He shook her again. 'I ought to give you a damned good hiding! Lost! You came out here without a thought to what I'd said—deliberately disobeying my orders! I can't believe it.'

'I'm so very sorry....' Her voice faltered as another figure came into view. 'I've caused such a lot of trouble——'

'Come on!' Roughly Kort took her arm and almost jerked her off her feet. 'David,' he said to the other man who had just arrived, 'fetch the utility.'

'Yes, Boss!'

Still grasping her arm. Kort propelled her along in the wake of David, who was hurrying to fetch the vehicle. Five minutes later, without another word having passed between them, Sally and Kort were in the utility, being driven to the homestead by the stockman. Soon other lights were appearing, and other vehicles coming along. Sally, overwhelmed by guilt and contrition, spoke at last, feeling she had to say something.

'All this trouble—Kort, I'm so very sorry, and ashamed. I didn't do it deliberately, as you said, but there was no excuse, for all that. I should have remembered all you'd told me and....' Her voice trailed off to an unhappy silence, for Kort was staring straight ahead and even in the darkness she could discern the formidable lines of his profile. 'What can I say to make amends——?'

'Make amends?' he interrupted, and for the first time since she had known him she heard a harshness in his voice. 'Do you suppose for one moment you can make amends for all the trouble you've caused? These men have been out of their beds all night! Their wives are also searching—close to the homestead. Every adult on the station has been put to extreme inconvenience by your disregard of the most important rule of the Outback: you do *not* wander away from the homestead!'

She fell silent, swiftly removing the tears as they fell. For should Kort see them he would not hesitate to make some scathing comment about self-pity.

The sun was coming up as they reached the homestead, rising from behind a hill with a flourish of russet and tawny gold, but the spectacular splendour of combined colours had no attraction for Sally this morning. Weighed down by the enormity of her offence and the knowledge that Kort would never be able to pardon it, she merely murmured a quiet 'thank you, Kort,' and went up to her bedroom where, despite her exhaustion, she lay awake hour after hour, never having been so crushed in spirit in the whole of her life.

CHAPTER NINE

It was five o'clock in the afternoon when Sally left her room. She would have done anything not to go downstairs at all that day, but at four o'clock Kort had sent Susannah up with the message that he wanted to see Sally in his study some time between five and six o'clock. She decided to get it over and done with, and so it was only a couple of minutes past five when she knocked quietly on Kort's door.

'Come in.' Abrupt the tone, and hard the features as she entered, pausing uncertainly just inside the doorway. 'Sit down.' A flick of Kort's hand indicated the chair at the opposite side of his desk. Sally felt like some wretched little culprit of a schoolgirl who had been sent to the headmaster for punishment. 'Well?' said Kort, 'have you nothing to say?'

'What is there to say?' she whispered. 'I feel so awful that I want to bury my head somewhere.'

He frowned suddenly and a little of his austerity seemed to evaporate.

'What exactly happened?' he inquired curiously.

'You won't understand,' she began, when he interrupted her, repeating his question. Sally shrugged helplessly. 'It's so difficult to explain,' she said. 'I myself can't understand what happened.'

'Nonsense! Answer my question.'

'After you'd left me I didn't feel like coming back here——'

'Why didn't you?' he interrupted.

Sally looked at him, noting the curiosity mingling with the hardness in his eyes. The sun was slanting through the window, throwing his bronzed features into relief and highlighting the threads of silver at his temples. How distinguished he looked! Sally felt a dim stirring of an emotion that was by no means unfamiliar to her, an emotion that was profoundly disturbing ... and no longer indefinable. She was in love with this stern-faced man who was sitting like a judge who had already decided on the sentence.

He was intending to send her back to England just as soon as it could be arranged.

'I felt unhappy,' she admitted at last.

'Because of your rudeness to me?'

Sally nodded her head.

'I shouldn't have allowed myself to be carried away like that.'

A moment of silence followed, as Kort frowned in thought. However, he let that pass and asked again why she had gone out into the bush.

'It seems so incredible that you would lose sight of the house,' he added, and Sally nodded in agreement.

'It seems incredible to me too,' she said, her wide clear gaze clearly telling him that she was as puzzled as he. 'I wanted to ride, and I took a path which looked inviting—but I meant to keep the homestead, or the bungalows, in sight. Really I did.'

Kort uttered a sigh of exasperation, but the depth of anger she had expected was certainly not in evidence. How strange, she thought. She had fully expected a severe and ruthless dressing down, but instead, Kort seemed anxious to learn the reason for what she had done.

'If you wanted to keep the homestead in sight, then

why didn't you?' he inquired logically at length.

'I was deep in thought as I rode along——' She stopped, shrugging helplessly. 'It's one of those things which will always remain a puzzle to me,' she added lamely, her eyes pleading as they looked across the desk to meet his. She was begging for understanding, even while owning to herself that she had no right to expect him to understand anything so absurd as that kind of behaviour, more especially as she could not understand it herself.

He remained silent for a long while, toying with a pen which he drew absently over a blotter. Sally spoke at last, saying in low and husky tones,

'I know you'll want me to leave at once. I'm quite prepared to do so. Nicole will have to do as I ask.'

To her surprise no nod of agreement followed her words. Instead, Kort seemed to give a slight start and frown inwardly.

'I don't want you to leave,' he told her quietly, and something in his tone caused her heart to leap.

'But—but—I fully expected——'

'I promised you a trip to the Alice,' he broke in softly. 'We'll go just as soon as I can arrange it.'

'We?' Her eyes were wide and questioning. 'You said that Ray would be taking Nicole and me.'

'A day or two's relaxation won't do me any harm,' he said.

'You're very kind. . . .' She looked mistily at him. 'I don't know why you're not—not angry.'

'I am angry, Sally. Make no mistake about that.'

'And yet you still want me here, as your guest?' She looked bewilderedly at him. 'I don't understand why you should—after all the trouble I've caused to everyone.'

Kort's features remained expressionless as he said,
'It should be enough that I still want you to stay
here, at Grey River Downs, as my guest.'

She could not fathom him at all. But a lightness
within her had taken away some of the sense of guilt
with which she had been weighed down. For it would
seem that Kort was prepared to let the matter drop
and never to mention it again.

'What did Kort have to say to you?' Nicole was asking in an awed voice a short while later, after Sally had
given her a brief explanation of how she came to be
lost. 'He was blazing mad this morning, and if you
hadn't gone off to bed I think he'd have given you a
good shaking—or something.'

Sally coloured.

'He'd already given me one,' she confessed.

'He had? When?'

'As soon as he found me—well, not immediately,'
she added, subsiding into a reflective mood. 'It was
only after I'd assured him that I wasn't hurt at all. At
first, he seemed very concerned indeed.'

'He did?' Nicole looked curiously at her. 'But then,
when he knew you were all right, he became angry?'

'Furiously angry,' replied Sally with a visible shud-
der.

'I wonder. . . .'

'Yes? What do you wonder?'

Nicole hesitated, but not for long.

'I believe he likes you,' she said.

Sally's eyelashes came down. She herself had experienced a vestige of optimism just now, since it did
occur to her that the only explanation of Kort's toler-
ant attitude was that he had come to like her ... to
like her in one special way.

'It's too much to hope for,' she said, but to herself. Aloud she feigned surprise, telling Nicole not to be silly.

'He's a confirmed bachelor, remember?'

'Many men have been confirmed bachelors and then fallen in love.'

'He told me quite recently that his preference is for complete freedom.'

'Yes? How did a thing like that come into the conversation?'

'We were talking about the girl he was once engaged to.'

'Gracia? Ray hoped they'd get together again, but he was disappointed. Kort had eyes for no one but you.'

'Nonsense!' flashed Sally, but her colour deepened for all that.

'I said at the time that he gave you most of his attention that night. Apart for those few dances he had with one or two of the other girls he spent the whole evening with you.' A pause, but Sally did not speak. 'And he took you for a walk in the dark!' An odd expression had settled on Nicole's face and Sally was not surprised when at length she added, 'Did he kiss you ... or anything?'

Sally's colour became more pronounced than ever.

'What a question to ask——!' she began, but Nicole interrupted, clapping her hands together.

'He did! It's written all over your face! You're a dark horse, Sally! Oh, but I'm glad. Mind, I wish it were me he'd fallen for,' she added with a touch of mischief in her voice, 'but as long as it isn't I'm thrilled that it's you. I think I shall have to give you a little hug!'

155

'You'll do no such thing! You're going far too quickly, Nicole. If Kort does like me than he's yet to reveal the fact.'

'It's obvious! Tell me, what did he say to you just now? I'll wager he didn't scold you severely at all.'

'No,' admitted Sally, 'he didn't—which surprised me very much indeed.'

'Shall I tell you why he didn't scold you?' Nicole waited for Sally's answer but, receiving none, she continued, 'He's too relieved that you weren't thrown from that horse. I didn't see him when Marengo returned, but Ray told me his brother went quite pale, and he seemed terribly agitated. Ray said he had never seen him lose his composure before—not once.' Again Nicole paused. 'It's plain now that he was out of his mind with anxiety, but at the time both Ray and I took it for granted that he was just ordinarily concerned—in the way he would be were it anyone else who was missing.'

'Have you heard from Robert today?' inquired Sally, abruptly changing the subject, as it was becoming too embarrassing by far. 'You've spoken to him over the air?'

'Yes—for a long time!' Nicole's face became animated; she instantly forgot the previous conversation. 'He'd have stayed on the air all day if I'd let him.'

Sally said, glancing a little disdainfully at her,

'You used to be so sensible. I can't think what's come over you.'

Nicole merely grinned.

'Robert could be fun, Sally.'

'Is he so very different from Ray?'

'They're poles apart as regards personality. Ray's—well—he's the stolid type. Oh, I know what you're

156

going to say. You're going to remind me that I myself am of a serious nature. Yes, I admit it, but I want some fun out of life as well. Everyone should be able to relax, should know when to work and when to play. Ray's been domineered by his brother far too long. He ought to take over his own place—Walleroo Creek—and make his own life.'

'I'm not so sure I agree with you when you assert that Kort's domineered over Ray. He's had to be his guardian, remember.'

'Well....' Nicole gave a little shrug of her shoulders. 'Perhaps you're right, Sally, but the time has come for Ray to break away, don't you think?'

Sally had to admit that she was inclined to agree with Nicole about this, but she did add that Ray had not the same strength of character as that possessed by his brother and therefore he was having difficulty in breaking away.

'I don't believe he'll do it until he gets married,' she said finally.

'If Kort should get married he might tell Ray to move out of Grey River Downs,' began Nicole, but was instantly sidetracked by Sally's reverting to the subject of Robert who, said Sally, was not to be taken seriously.

'You're just a diversion for him,' she pointed out. 'Life here can be dull for a young man, so naturally he'll seize the opportunity of brightening it up a little.'

'There are plenty of pretty girls he could amuse himself with,' returned Nicole at once. 'He says he's never been interested—until now.'

'Nicole—you can't have fallen in love with each other!'

'We certainly like each other——' Nicole paused in

157

thought. 'Given time, we could become much more than mere friends.'

'Well, you haven't the time.' Sally reminded her.

'Kort doesn't want us to go yet.'

'I don't expect he'll want us to stay too long,' said Sally in an expressionless tone, and a slow smile broke over Nicole's face.

'If he's fallen for you, love, he'll not want you to be going yet awhile. And when you do go he'll ask—no, *command*—you to return without any unnecessary delay.'

Sally frowned darkly at her, and told her to let the subject drop, once and for all.

'All right—if it's so embarrassing for you,' returned Nicole obligingly. 'In any case, I must go and give myself a manicure. I can't appear at the dinner-table with hands like these. I've been doing a bit of gardening this afternoon.'

No sooner had Nicole gone than Ray appeared. Sally and Nicole had been sitting on a little rustic seat beside the summer-house and Sally had the impression that Ray had been in the vicinity for some time. His first words revealed that her impression was correct.

'I've been waiting for a chance to speak to you alone, Sally. It's about Nicole.'

'Yes?' Sally's eyes flickered to his face, noticing the rather sulky pull at the corners of his mouth.

'She's no right to be going off for a whole day with Robert Shaw!'

Startled by his sudden anger, which was so uncharacteristic of him, Sally found herself recalling Kort's suggestion that Nicole might be attempting to make Ray jealous.

'I can't see any harm in it,' she returned guardedly. 'She doesn't know him!'

'They were together quite a lot at the dance,' was Sally's reminder, and she could not resist adding, 'You did neglect her, you know.'

He bit his lip, looking more sulky than ever.

'It was Dora. I couldn't ignore her, could I?'

'No, of course not, but neither could you expect Nicole to sit there watching you giving another girl your attention. It was Nicole you took to the dance and therefore it was incumbent on you to see that she was not left on her own for too long.'

'Like Kort with you,' he muttered almost to himself, and presumably diverted for the moment. 'But his relationship with Gracia was different from mine with Dora.' A thoughtful pause ensued before he added, on a distinct note of impatience, 'I wish he'd been different with Gracia. If he married her I wouldn't have to inherit Grey River Downs.' He looked down at Sally, then at the space on the seat just a short while ago vacated by Nicole.

'Do you want to sit down, Ray?'

'For a few minutes. I wanted to talk about Nicole, wanted to ask you to tell her she's not to go to Pedamooka with Robert.'

'Nicole pleases herself, Ray.'

'Do you agree with what she's doing?'

'Not altogether,' she replied frankly. 'Nevertheless, as I've just implied, I'm in no position to interfere in Nicole's actions.'

He seemed to scrape his teeth together.

'I hate the idea of her being with him!'

'So you're jealous,' she said perceptively, wondering what Kort would have to say about this. In all probability he would refuse to believe that Nicole had no thought of making Ray jealous.

'I suppose you could call it jealousy.'

'But you've decided you don't want to marry Nicole.'

'Because of Kort, that's all.'

Sally shook her head.

'You don't really want to marry Nicole, Ray. This is just a dog-in-the-manger attitude which in my opinion is exceedingly childish.'

His mouth tightened.

'If we'd had no interference——'

'You'd both have ruined your lives. You and Nicole are just not suited to one another.'

'Well, I shan't marry Dora, and I've told Kort as much!'

'You'll meet the right girl one day,' she told him in gentle tones.

'Perhaps—but meanwhile I'm controlled by my brother.'

'That's not true,' she returned, anxious to defend Kort. 'You could go to your own cattle station to-morrow if you wished.'

A small silence followed and then, in the most firm and decisive voice she had ever heard him use,

'I shall do just that, Sally! Yes, I'll show him I have a will of my own!'

'I have an idea that will please him, Ray.'

His profile had been towards her, but now he swung round.

'You have?' he said in surprise.

'It's my belief that he would like you to stand on your own feet. After all, no one wants to retain responsibility for the welfare of someone else if he can possibly avoid it. I feel Kort will admire you for this decision you've just made.'

'Well!' he ejaculated. 'And I've always been reluctant to take over Walleroo Creek because I felt he would be hurt if I left here.'

'I should discuss it with him first, though,' she advised. 'It wouldn't be very nice if you just packed up and departed.'

'No, you're very right. I'll have a chat with him this evening after dinner.'

'You feel better now?'

He smiled then and said ruefully,

'I was so mad at the idea of Nicole going off with Robert, but I have to agree with you that she and I are not sufficiently suited for us to be contemplating marriage.' He looked happy, as if he had been freed from some irksome restraint on his liberty. 'I'm glad we had this little talk, Sally,' he said after a pause. 'By the way, Kort tells me you're not leaving yet awhile?' He looked at her as she shook her head. 'It's Gracia,' he added musingly, and Sally shot him a swift interrogating glance.

'Gracia?'

'Kort was so sure she'd leave here at once and return to Sydney. But she didn't. You'll recall that both you and I suspected Kort of—well—using you, as you yourself termed it, to make Gracia believe he had another interest. Apparently she's not deceived and she's staying, hoping that she can get Kort after all. If you'd left it would have proved her right in her assumption that there's nothing serious between you. And so he's had to ask you to stay on. I expect he'll be willing for you to leave as soon as Gracia has accepted the fact that there's no hope for her at all. . . .'

Ray's voice trailed away and he gave her a searching look as he became aware of Sally's changing expression. 'Is anything wrong?' he inquired innocently. 'You've gone quite pale.'

'No—there's n-nothing wrong,' she answered, forcing a smile. 'Er—how do you know all this about Gracia?'

'She told someone she wasn't convinced that Kort had another girl. She firmly believes that the reason he's never married is that he still loves her.' Ray gave a grin and added, little knowing the deep hurt he was inflicting upon his companion, 'It was a bit of luck for Kort that you appeared on the scene. It's certainly made things easy for him. Gracia is bound to admit, in a little while, that she hasn't a Buckley. She'll then depart and Kort will feel satisfied that he's handled the situation very cleverly. He didn't want to have anything unfriendly develop between himself and her father, you see.'

Sally made no comment; she was lost in bitter reflection, squirming inwardly at her own optimism in daring to hope that Kort would come to care for her. He was using her—nothing more nor less than this stark and undeniable fact filled all her mental capacity at this moment. Using her, for his own ends.... She had known, of course, but owing to his changed manner with her she had foolishly allowed this knowledge to slip into the far recesses of her mind. She reflected on the interview she had had with him an hour ago, recalling how puzzled she had been that he had neither admonished her nor asked her to leave.

'It should be enough that I still desire you to stay here, at Grey River Downs, as my guest,' he had answered when she had questioned him as to his reason. And she, fool that she was, had suddenly known a lightness of spirit and dared to cherish the thought that he wanted her to stay for a different reason altogether. Nicole, too, believed he was beginning to have an affection for her. Again Sally squirmed inwardly as she dwelt on her embarrassment when she had to tell Nicole that Kort had been using her for his own ends and that he had never come anywhere near to caring for her.

That evening Sally deliberately adopted a cold and impersonal manner towards Kort, and for one long period she preserved an austere silence. He seemed puzzled, which was not surprising, and she guessed he would have questioned her openly had not his brother requested a private talk with him as soon as the meal was finished.

The following morning Nicole went off early, Robert's plane having arrived at the airstrip before eight o'clock.

'I still think she ought not to be going.' Ray spoke to Sally as they both turned back to the homestead, having gone over to the airstrip to see the couple off.

Having fully expected him to bring up the subject of her escapade, Sally was relieved to find his whole attention was on Nicole.

'Robert will take good care of her,' she responded, then asked how he had fared last evening with his brother.

'He was delighted,' he answered, suddenly brightening. 'It would seem that he's been waiting a long while for me to assert myself. Isn't it strange that I never guessed? I was always so scared of offending him.'

'I'm glad it all went off as you both wanted it to. When are you leaving Grey River Downs?'

'In about two weeks' time. There are things to do. Meanwhile, though, I must go over to Walleroo Creek, just to warn everyone that I'm taking over.' He stopped, his brow creased in thought. 'It'll be rather nice to be called the boss, and have everyone respecting me in the way they respect my brother here.' He was very young, she thought, and she rather hoped that even when he had taken over as the boss of Walleroo Creek Kort would be there to help if Ray should seek his help.

Kort was at the paddock as they came back. Just about to leave for the far valley and the cattle run, he was in the saddle, a proud arresting figure sitting on an equally proud and arresting mount. His gaze as it came to rest on Sally's upturned face was piercing and, she thought, a little baffled.

'Why weren't you at breakfast?' he wanted to know. 'Nicole was there.'

'I wasn't hungry,' answered Sally stiffly. She *had* been hungry, but, after a restless night during which Ray's words hovered on the edge of her mind even when she was dozing, she found she had no desire at all to face Kort across the breakfast table and act as if nothing had happened. She was too potently aware of his using her, just as if she had been some inanimate object without feelings or emotions.

'You weren't?' Still piercing those eyes, with their little network of lines fanning out in the most attractive way. His slouch hat, pushed to the back of his head, allowed the grey threads at his temples to catch the sun, so that they shone like strands of silver. His face was rugged, sun-toughened and burnt to the tawny hue of an Arab's; his checked shirt was open at the throat, revealing more bronzed and toughened skin. 'Have you had a bad night or something?'

She averted her head, embarrassed because Ray was watching the little scene with an odd kind of interest and because Kort himself seemed determined to make her provide him with a satisfactory reason for her non-appearance at the breakfast-table.

'I slept fitfully,' she offered at last, and saw him frown.

'You weren't well?'

She looked up, her beautiful, elfin-like features revealing all the bewilderment she felt. Why should he be so persistent? Had this occurred before Ray had spoken those shattering words last evening she would have been experiencing profound pleasure, prepared to believe that Kort's questions were born of concern for her well-being. But not now. She meant nothing to him—— No, that was not quite correct. She was of use to him, in a very practical way.

'I was well,' she told him at last, 'but for some reason I didn't sleep much at all.'

'I think I'd better be off, if you two will excuse me?' Ray spoke quickly, inserting the words before his brother could comment on what Sally had just said. Kort gave him a cursory glance and nodded his head.

'Tell Caswell we're cutting out the clearskins from the mob, I'll be along shortly.'

'I will.' Ray mounted the horse which the Abo rouseabout had ready and within seconds he was cantering away towards the undulating slopes of the cattle run. Kort's eyes, narrowed against the sun's bright rays, followed him for a brief moment before returning to examine Sally's face.

'Something's happened,' he stated, his jaw flexed. 'What is it?'

'Nothing——'

'Don't lie, Sally! If you knew me better you'd hesitate at trying my patience. Yesterday, in my study, you were very different from what you were later, at dinner, when you were scarcely civil. This morning you're no better. If you've a complaint to make then let's have it. I've no time for beating about the bush.'

She stared at him in amazement; he might have been her husband, so authoritative was his manner.

'I haven't a complaint, Kort,' she said, forgetting, for the moment, her intention of treating him coldly. 'I don't understand you at all?'

'Nor I you,' was his snap rejoinder. 'However, we don't seem to be getting anywhere, so I'll be off. Have a pleasant day.' And with that he gave the horse its head and galloped away, he and the horse forming a magnificent picture etched as they were against the dark mass of the distant mountains. Sally's eyes filled, and she felt a hurtful constriction in her throat.

She had not minded too much that he was using her—not after that first stab of indignation. She herself was not suffering any harm by it. She had understood just what Kort was trying to do—and she recalled her reluctance to cause him embarrassment by telling Gracia that there was nothing between her and Kort. Kort himself had been totally confident that she would not let him down. Yes, he had actually relied on her ... and she now realized that his trust, amounting to flattery, had brought her a little access of sheer pleasure. How little she had realized at that time that she would fall in love with him! Yet, upon reflection, she had to confess that almost from the very beginning Kort Lander had held a profound attraction for her. He was too handsome by far, too attractively masculine—a man of the great outdoors, a man at home in the saddle, a man born to command. It was no wonder she had fallen in love with him, she thought, yet at the same time deprecating herself for her foolishness, since she had been informed by Kort himself that his preference was for complete freedom. Such a man would never fall in love simply because he had no intention of marrying.

She was still standing where Kort had left her and presently the Abo rouseabout asked her if she wanted Marengo saddling. She said yes, thanking him when he brought the horse over to her.

She swung into the saddle and cantered away, her back to the cattle run and the mountains beyond. Her mind wandered, but she was fully alert to the danger of going too far. She made for the cut-off meander—the billabong around which grew the casuarinas and the kurrajong trees, these latter the doyens of the Inland. Its uses were numerous, Ray had told her. Not only was it a marvellous shade-maker but it was also highly drought-resistant. It made good stock feed as well. Sally tethered the pony and sat down, watching it graze the blue grass. The area around about the billabong was particularly pretty, with the water, the trees and grasses all contributing to a softness and a colour harmony not seen very often in this particular region. How quiet it all was! Sally found to her surprise that she was enjoying the peace and tranquillity despite the heaviness which lay over her heart. She naturally thought of Kort's promise to take her and Nicole to Alice Springs and debated whether or not to refuse—

should his offer still stand, of course. As things were between them at present she would not be in the least surprised if he had changed his mind. But she was soon to learn that his promise still stood. She and he met at lunch time, taking the meal informally on the verandah.

'I've arranged to have three days off work beginning the day after tomorrow,' he said without preamble as soon as an opportunity arose. 'I trust this will meet with your approval?'

'Yes,' she murmured, but hesitantly. She ought to refuse, she decided, but instead she found herself actually becoming enthusiastic as Kort went on to talk of the many attractions of this oasis in the Outback, a town set amid the red and mauve MacDonnell Ranges in the dead centre of Australia.

'It will be an experience you won't forget,' he went on finally. 'I hope you'll both enjoy it.'

'I'm sure we shall.' Her pensive gaze had been occupied by the familiar scene of stockriders and the healthy Brahmin cattle grazing the low hills, but she turned her clear, slanting eyes towards him as she spoke. 'Thank you, Kort, for offering to take us.' He said nothing; she managed the ghost of a smile but her voice was crisply impersonal as she added, 'It'll be something to talk about when we get back home.'

Silence ... unfathomable and profound. She watched his jaw flex, his mouth go tight, saw with some degree of puzzlement that a nerve was pulsating at one side of his throat. It was a tense interlude; Sally's nerves became on edge and she glanced away, inexplicably avoiding his eyes. The sun, high in the sky, created bizarre colours over the landscape of prickly, waist-high porcupine grass, but on the mountains its pure unhindered flow was like sparkling champagne. Her eyes moved, to the closer, haunting loveliness of the gardens of the homestead. Bougainvillaea rioted over walls and trellises; azaleas, poinsettias, camellias and numerous other exotic flowers compounded to create an incredible admixture of colour and perfume that was both exquisite and heady.

She turned at length, as if forced to do so by the strength of Kort's will. His stare was inflexible, austere and unsmiling. It seemed to be expressionless and yet, paradoxically, Sally sensed in it a mingling of censure and pain. Pain.... She frowned to herself, the idea occurring to her that perhaps after all Kort was hurt by his brother's decision to leave Grey River Downs and take up the management of his own place, Walleroo Creek. Obviously Kort would not have allowed Ray to guess that he was hurt, hence Ray's enthusiastic statement that his brother was delighted at his decision. Yes, reasoned Sally, Kort *was* upset by Ray's decision. Well, that was very strange, because she could have sworn that he would have received his brother's news both with satisfaction and relief.

Suddenly the silence was shattered by the raucous laughter of a couple of jackos sitting on the branch of a nearby tree. Sally heaved a sigh of relief. The sweet course for which they had been waiting arrived and for the rest of the meal no further words passed between them. It was a most uncomfortable few moments and Sally guessed that Kort was as relieved as she when at last the meal was over and they parted company, Sally to go to her room, Kort to ride off to supervise the mustering of several thousand clearskins for branding.

CHAPTER TEN

RAY was accompanying them and he it was who piloted the plane on the flight to Alice Springs. He had asked if he could take over the controls and without hesitation Kort allowed him to do so; this was in order to give him more practice, Sally realized, for soon now he would be piloting his own plane all the time.

'Isn't it spectacular!' exclaimed Sally, looking down on to a sunlit landscape fashioned by eons of erosion and, later, the deposition of Lower Paleozoic sediments. Among the mulga and spinifex scrub there roamed mobs of kangaroos, flourishing among these spiky, inhospitable grasses, and, of course, to add to the scene were the cattle, from other vast stations, and the tough parchment-faced stockriders whose lives were spent in the saddle, under the merciless Australian sun.

Kort, sitting beside Sally, turned his head and commented in cool and slowly-drawn-out tones,

'Most people would find our scenery monotonous. After all, it is semi-desert down there.' Something in his manner caused a tenseness within her, and as a result her own manner was even more chill and impersonal than she had actually intended.

'It wouldn't do for everyone to think alike. What pleases the eye of one man or woman would probably be regarded as entirely uninteresting by another.'

Kort flashed her an inscrutable glance and then

turned his head, looking down as if his attention had suddenly been caught by something. Sally bit her lip, vexed that her mind should be so confused and unmanageable. She had no patience with her bouts of indecision as to how she intended treating Kort. One moment she wanted to treat him with near-indifference, while the next she found herself yearning for that friendly companionship which had been theirs so recently, this after a start during which they both agreed to being enemies.

Nicole was chatting to Ray; they at least appeared to be able to adapt themselves to the new position which had developed as a result of their agreement not to marry. Nicole had confided earlier, at breakfast, that she wished it were Robert who was coming with them to Alice Springs.

'We had such a wonderful day at Padamooka,' she had added, her face glowing at the memory, 'as I described to you afterwards. Robert's rather special!'

Sally had not troubled to ask again what could possibly come of the relationship. She was too involved in her own unhappy state to want to concern herself with Nicole's affairs. She supposed another pen-friendship would develop, but further than this she could not see.

'Oh, what's that?' Nicole was pointing downwards; both men spoke together.

'A dust storm,' and Kort added that it was not by any means a severe one. Another few miles and then Nicole spoke again, pointing out the camp-fire where stockmen would be making flour damper and billy tea. Another scene was that of roos drinking from a granite soak; this led Ray to explain how the roos could sense just where the thunderstorms would occur.

'The whole mob then makes for the region,' he

171

went on. 'We say they're "on the wallaby", which means they're going to the area of rain to seek more palatable food.'

'Isn't it uncanny how they know where the rain is going to be?' said Sally incredulously.

'An instinct peculiar to those whose food supply depends on the climate,' interposed Kort languidly.

Some of the animals were moving from the drinking-place and Sally watched them, fascinated by their superb balance and rhythmic spring. Soon they were left behind as signs of human activity gave evidence of another cattle station. The homestead appeared—a white wooden box with others sprawling around it. A utility bounced up and down on a dry creek bed; a stockman could be discerned having a struggle with a brumbie; a couple of white-aproned women stood in the middle of a paved yard and waved to those in the plane. Then the undulating cattle runs and finally nothing again but the brown and dusty wilderness.

'So many changes of scene,' murmured Sally almost to herself, and Kort turned his head. She looked down, feeling awkward as her colour rose; she did not want him to see it. Even yet again there was a change in scene, with thickets of tangled wild wattle and mallee gums interspersed with areas of harsh grey scrub and tall prickly grasses. Another mob of kangaroos came into view, protected from the heat of the day by the spreading bushes under which they had made their dust holes. A flock of galahs rose above the animals, the glorious colour of their breasts forming a cloud of salmon-pink which contrasted with dramatic effect with the grey-green hues of the acacia scrubland.

'There she is,' Ray spoke into the long silence which had prevailed during the latter part of the journey. 'The Alice!'

The town was there, coming closer all the time, the only town for hundreds of miles in any direction, a town where the River Todd roared through its streets for only one short period in the year, and for the rest of the time it was dry, for there was only ten inches of rain per year in this, the red centre of the continent.

Their hotel was luxurious, with air-conditioning and a large, tree-shaded swimming pool. The two girls shared a bedroom which had an enormous picture window giving on to a broad terrace overlooking the gardens.

'Kort's arranged several trips for us, hasn't he?' Nicole was excited at the prospect of seeing the dramatic spectacle of Ayers Rock and the caves around its base. 'We'll be off tomorrow immediately after breakfast.'

Sally nodded her head; she was not too happy at the idea of Kort's being put to so great an expense. The atmosphere between them had so deteriorated on the flight that she hated the idea of his paying out any money at all for her entertainment. The hotel bill itself would be big enough, but to have him pay for trips as well. . . .

However, unable to see any way out, she had no alternative other than to resign herself to an acceptance of the situation.

Dinner was a pleasant meal despite the real coldness which characterized Kort's behaviour towards Sally. Fortunately neither Ray nor Nicole seemed to notice, being absorbed in conversation with one another for most of the time. After dinner there was dancing in

173

the hotel ballroom and Sally found herself in Kort's arms, dancing in absolute silence. Unable to bear it any longer, she tried to open a conversation, but as Kort answered only in monosyllables she soon abandoned the attempt.

The following morning they took the tour to Ayers Rock, an awesome residual greater in area than the City of London. From there they travelled by coach to Mount Olga, composed of fantastically coloured rocks and ravines which rose from the spinifex plains.

That evening they all sat out in the garden of the hotel, enjoying the cool breeze that was drawn in from the mountains. But Ray and Nicole went off after a time and, much to her dismay, Sally found herself alone with Kort.

'Would you like to walk too?' he inquired tersely and, it seemed, without much interest. 'Or do you prefer to go to bed? It's been a long day.'

She hesitated a moment, afraid of saying the wrong thing. She said at length that she preferred to stay where she was.

'But you,' she added swiftly, 'what do you want to do?'

He shrugged indifferently.

'I'm all right here.'

She said, because she felt she must,

'I can't help thinking that you've been inconvenienced by bringing us here.'

'I made a promise to bring you,' he reminded her, lifting a lean bronzed hand to stifle a yawn. The lights were on in the hotel grounds, coloured lights which lent romance to the whole aspect of palms and flowers and soft music drifting out from the open windows of the hotel. Sally could not help thinking of what might have been had Kort come to care for her.

She looked at him now, noting the stern set features, made harder by the darkness of his skin and the lean, angular bone structure which itself was accentuated by the height of the cheekbones and the hollows beneath. His eyes, keen and clear, met hers and they too were hard—and expressionless.

'I know you made a promise,' she said, 'but somehow I've gained the impression that you later wanted to change your mind.'

'If I'd wanted to change my mind I'd have done so,' was his terse rejoinder.

'Yes,' she murmured, deflated.

'Just as a point of interest, what reason had you for gaining the impression that I wanted to change my mind?'

How could she answer that without mentioning the change which had taken place in their relationship?

'It was merely an impression,' she returned lamely.

'One doesn't form an impression without some cause.' His tone seemed suddenly to hold contempt, as if his opinion of her intelligence was not very high. She bristled, all her indignation that he should use her coming to the fore.

'I had a cause, but I prefer to keep it to myself.'

Silence. She looked away from him, towards the windows of the ballroom where couples in casual dress were enjoying a square dance.

'We appear,' said Kort with a flash of impatience, 'to be back where we started.'

'As enemies?' The two words escaped from Sally's lips unbidden and she would have taken them back if that were possible.

'Most certainly we're not *friends*.' Anger now

175

kindled his eyes and his jaw was flexed. 'I've never met a woman as unfathomable as you.'

She stared, bewildered by his attitude, which was so uncharacteristic of the haughty boss of Grey River Downs. If it were not too absurd to be a possibility she would have begun to wonder if her chill aloofness had piqued him. He was looking at her, waiting for her to offer some response to his words. She fumbled, completely at a loss, and so she changed the subject, saying she would like to take a stroll, after all. Kort's lips twisted in a humourless smile and he rose instantly.

'As you wish,' he assented, and stood while she picked up her small pearl-trimmed evening bag.

'What a beautiful night it is.' Her words came softly, giving no evidence of her frayed nerves. 'The stars are wonderful.'

He glanced upwards, to where the Southern Cross flared against the deep purple of the sky.

'Some people wouldn't notice.'

She nodded in agreement.

'I often look at the sky at home. Of course, there are many stars which you see that we can't.'

'Naturally.' So cool the tone ... and yet she sensed something strangely gentle about it which filled her with a deep yearning which she thrust from her consciousness, angry with herself for desiring what she could not have.

'I want to go back,' she said abruptly. 'I find I'm too tired for walking.'

Kort stopped and, as if losing control of his patience for a moment, he took her chin in his hand and roughly turned her face up. It was pale in the moonlight, and her lips trembled. His touch, ungentle as it was, sent exquisite tinglings through her whole body. Although despising herself for it, she admitted she wanted nothing more than his arms about her, and his lips on hers.

'What's the matter with you?' he demanded. 'First you don't want to walk, and then you do! Then you want to go back because you're tired. What's the matter with you?' he repeated, and it did seem that he would shake her, as he had done on the night she was lost. What an unpredictable man he was!—losing control like this. She would never have believed it possible. 'I've asked you a question, Sally! What the devil's got into you that you're so sulky and quarrelsome!'

'I'm neither sulky or quarrelsome——' She twisted away, tears gathering in her eyes. 'I w-want to—to go back to the hotel....'

They had been back at Grey River Downs two days when Sally told Nicole she was ready to go home.

'I'm asking Kort to see about the flight,' she added. 'I expect Ray will fly us to the airport.'

A sudden frown appeared on Nicole's forehead.

'I've been talking to Robert twice a day over the air, Sally, and—and he's very anxious that I stay——'

'I want to go home, Nicole.' Sally spoke in so dejected a tone that it was bound to arrest Nicole's attention. She looked searchingly into her eyes for a long moment before saying,

'Kort—you and he have quarrelled?'

'I'd rather not discuss Kort.'

'I see.... So he hasn't fallen for you. But you—you've fallen for——'

'Nicole,' Sally interrupted impatiently, 'I'm not

177

staying here any longer!'

'Because you love Kort and he doesn't love you. I can understand, Sally, and I'm very sorry. I thought it would be wonderful if you and he got married.'

Genuine regret brought a brightness to Nicole's eyes. But she said no more, aware as she was of the embarrassment which Sally was suffering.

'I must go, Nicole.' It was Sally who eventually broke the long silence. 'You do agree about that?'

Again Nicole frowned.

'Surely you can stay just a little while longer? Robert and I do like each other—— No, please don't interrupt,' she begged and, watching her expression, Sally suddenly knew that Nicole really was in love this time. 'Robert will propose to me very soon,' went on Nicole. 'I'm quite sure of it.'

A small silence ensued, Sally's own brow puckering in a frown as she thought of her foster-mother's re-action to this new and unexpected turn of events.

'I just don't know what to say, Nicole. Obviously you're going to please yourself, but you must admit it's rather a hasty decision you're making?'

But Nicole was firmly shaking her head.

'This time it's real, Sally. I never felt like this with Ray—oh, I know I said I was in love with him, and I admit I believed I was.' She paused then and looked earnestly into Sally's troubled eyes. 'This is different,' she said quietly at last, and there certainly was no vestige of doubt in her voice. 'Both Robert and I know that it's the real thing.'

Sally gave a sigh, shrugging as she did so.

'I can't stay, love,' she said, a catch in her voice. 'It would be too much of a strain.'

'What I can't understand,' mused Nicole as the

thought occurred to her, 'is why Kort should be so anxious for you to stay on here.' She paused in concentration, then lifted her eyes to give Sally a strange glance. 'There must be some answer to that question.'

Sally hesitated, undecided as to whether or not she should enlighten Nicole fully. But no. It would be altogether too much. She had suffered enough embarrassment already.

'I expect he has his reasons,' she answered, hoping Nicole would let the matter drop. But she was to be disappointed.

'He has his reasons all right,' Nicole declared. 'A man like Kort never does anything without there being a good reason for it. He's in love with you,' she added confidently. 'I can see no other reason for——'

'Please!' Sally threw her an angry glance. 'That's enough. I'm not carrying on this discussion any longer!'

A small silence followed. Nicole's eyes narrowed strangely.

'Well,' she said at last, 'you can please yourself about that, of course, but you *cannot* please yourself about going home. You came here at Mum's request—to take care of me——'

'You don't need any taking care of,' broke in Sally, desperation edging her voice. 'I *have* to leave—as soon as possible!'

Receiving this with a calmness that infuriated Sally, Nicole made no reference to it as she said,

'What's Mum going to think of you if you go home alone?'

'I shall explain——'

'That you shirked your duty just because you yourself had fallen in love with Ray's brother and you couldn't stay on, even though you knew I was having an affair with a young man I'd met only three times?'

Sally stared at her in disbelief.

'I think you're horrid!' she exclaimed. 'If you cared anything at all about me you'd be only too willing to come home with me. You could conduct your court-ship with Robert by post,' she added, feeling just that tiny bit spiteful because, in her opinion, Nicole was being exceedingly unreasonable.

'If I cared anything about you?' Nicole smiled a little censoriously, and lifted her eyebrows in the strangest way. 'I think the world of you, Sally.' She looked directly into her eyes, conveying what was in her mind.

'I see....' So Nicole believe that Kort needed a little more time.... 'You mean well, Nicole, but——'

'Make no mistake,' interposed Nicole, 'although I think the world of you, I care for Robert much more.'

'And if I insist on going home you'll stay?'

Nicole nodded without hesitation.

'Yes, Sally, I will stay.'

'It would appear,' returned Sally in tones suddenly frigid, 'that you have me trapped.'

'I'm afraid so....' Nicole gave her a sweet smile, quite undaunted by the heavy frown she received in response. 'Because of that promise you made to my mother.'

A week passed; Nicole and Roger had been out three times and on the third occasion he proposed to her and she accepted him without hesitation.

'Well,' said Sally on the news of the engagement being imparted to her by Nicole, 'that now lets me out. I can go home.' The position between her and

Kort had neither improved nor deteriorated. They were civil to one another and that was all. She saw little of him, for he had gone off each morning and had remained out for the whole of the day, still taking part in the rounding up of thousands upon thousands of calves for branding. 'I expect you'll be coming home as well?' added Sally, with a questioning look at Nicole. 'And then you'll come back here to be married?'

'I haven't yet made up my mind,' replied Nicole uncommunicatively.

'You must have made some arrangements?' persisted Sally, but Nicole shook her head. Sally knew without any doubt at all that Nicole was desperately hoping for something to develop between herself and Kort. Well, it was wishful thinking on Nicole's part and, feeling she could now consider her own position, Sally made it her business to see Kort at the first opportunity.

After knocking on the door of his study one evening after dinner, she heard a curt 'come in' and entered, wasting no time at all in telling him what she wanted.

He had stood up on her entry, and now he frowned at her across the room, his tall formidable figure seeming to become stiff and tense.

'You want to leave at once?' He shook his head slightly, as if he hadn't really taken this in. 'This is sudden, isn't it? I thought we'd agreed that you were to stay on as my guest?'

'There was no question of my staying on indefinitely.'

'No.' A long silence followed; he was frowning heavily, and with the knowledge she had Sally experienced little difficulty in reading his thoughts. He was realizing that his plan regarding Gracia was about to collapse, and he would now be forced to inflict upon the girl the humiliation which he had tried so hard to avoid. His next words strengthened Sally's conclusions and at the same time brought a surge of anger rising within her, although she did manage to conceal this—for the present. 'It would please me if you stayed a little while longer, Sally.'

No doubt it would!

'I'm quite determined to leave,' she returned tautly, then added, 'I expect you know of the engagement between Nicole and Robert?'

'They're engaged?' His voice, like his face, was expressionless, but Sally sensed a hint of sardonic amusement within him. 'She did warn me that an engagement was imminent.' A small pause and then, 'What are her arrangements? Is she returning home and then coming back here?'

'I don't know yet. But for myself—I'm most anxious to leave just as soon as you can arrange it for me.'

Unexpectedly his mouth went tight.

'I'm exceedingly busy at the present time, Sally. I'm afraid you'll have to wait a while.'

'That's impossible, Kort.' She spoke quietly enough, but her growing anger was clearly betrayed by the quiver in her voice. 'My mind's made up.'

'And so is mine,' he told her curtly. 'I have important work to attend to for the next week or so, work which can't possibly be delayed.' His whole manner was officious and arrogant. 'I'm sorry, but you'll have to await my convenience.'

She stared, eyes blazing. Then something snapped within her, breaking all control.

'Await your convenience! No, I will not! Do you

suppose I'm such an idiot that I don't know why you want me here?—that I didn't know the reason for your inviting me to stay?' Her hands were tightly clenched at her sides and Kort's puzzled glance moved from them to her flushed face.

'You knew the reason for my wanting you to stay?'

'It was so that you could continue using me—in order to put Mrs Lester off! You said yourself you'd rather do it that way than cause her humiliation! But you didn't care about my feelings, did you? It didn't matter to you that I might be hurt——!' She broke off abruptly, all anger dissolved by dismay at what she had revealed. Yes, she had revealed quite plainly that she loved him. Tears of mortification gathered in her eyes and she swung round, groping for the door handle. 'Don't forget,' she managed with a note of command in her tone, 'I want to leave here immediately!' She found the handle, but never turned it. Covering the distance between them in a couple of easy strides, Kort seized her arm not too gently and swung her round to face him. 'Let me go!' she flashed. 'I——'

'It would appear,' he drawled, tightening his grip as she attempted to twist away, 'that there've been some major misunderstandings. Let's have the showdown, Sally, and then we might both be able to see straight.' Stern the voice, but it was the underlying hint of gentleness that caught and held Sally's attention, bringing an exquisite sense of warmth to her heart, a heart that had begun to beat far too quickly. Staring bewilderedly at him, she murmured in a voice husky with emotion,

'Your r-reason for w-wanting me to stay? Wasn't it because of Mrs Lester?'

Kort released her, his eyes regarding her with a strange mingling of tolerance and asperity.

'Mrs Lester left for her home in Sydney a few days after the shed dance.'

'Left?' breathed Sally, wide-eyed and disbelieving. 'She's gone?'

'She told someone that after seeing you she knew she hadn't a chance——'

'But Ray said . . .' Sally allowed her voice to trail off, unwilling to bring Ray into it. But of course Kort was quick to pursue the matter and in the end she had to tell him all that had happened. He let her continue, until she stopped, having related everything and, in the process, once again revealing her love for him.

Kort looked down at her in silence for a long moment before saying, with both tenderness and censure in his voice,

'You idiot, Sally! You should have known when I kissed you——'

'But you never—er—I mean . . .' She stopped, delightful colour flooding her face. Kort laughed and took her hand in his.

'Followed it up?' he returned quizzically. 'Well, my love, I must confess that I too have been an idiot. I tried to shut my eyes—and my heart—to what was happening to me. I told you I preferred my freedom and I confess I was enjoying it, so when a girl like you came along, bringing chaos to my most satisfactory mode of living, I naturally put up a defence.' He was laughing with his eyes and she thrilled to his attractiveness, and to his nearness, and to the exciting touch of his hand as he held her small one enclosed within it. 'I knew of course that you cared, knew by the way you responded to my kisses, because it was

184

always obvious to me that you weren't the kind of girl to indulge in an affair with anyone who just happened to be there.' He stopped, and she could not resist reminding him of his treatment of her when first she arrived. He only laughed and told her to forget it.

'What a time it's been,' he went on, entering into a reflective mood. 'There was I, wondering what on earth had happened, and beginning to doubt that you'd ever loved me, and there were you, believing all the wrong things. I could strangle Ray!' he ended with a sudden flash of anger.

'He was misinformed, obviously.'

'I can't see how.' Kort paused and frowned. 'But all comes over the air, and gossip has a habit of gathering twists and turns as it passes from mouth to mouth.'

Sally made no comment and for a while they talked, standing there, close together, holding hands. Small matters that had been puzzling to one or the other were brought up and straightened out. And then Sally found herself in Kort's arms, felt the strength of his body close to hers. She shone up at him, waiting for his kiss. Was it true? she kept on asking herself. Could the boss of Grey River Downs possibly love her, Sally Prentice, who had once heard him say that he was not interested in women?

'My heart tells me it's true,' she whispered, totally unaware that she spoke aloud. But her murmurings came through to Kort who, holding her at arm's length, gazed inquiringly into her eyes.

'What did you say?' he asked when she made no attempt to enlighten him.

She coloured, adorably confused.

'My heart tells me it's true,' she managed in a

husky, self-deprecating little voice, and a low laugh issued from Kort's lips before, sweeping her passionately into his arms, he sought her eager mouth with his.

Harlequin Collection Editions

Please note: The number in brackets indicates the original Harlequin Romance number.

Harlequin Collection Editions

Please note: The number in brackets indicates the original Harlequin Romance number.

Harlequin Collection Editions

*Please note: The number in brackets indicates the
original Harlequin Romance number.*

Harlequin Collection Editions

Please note: The number in brackets indicates the original Harlequin Romance number.

Complete and mail this coupon today!